Thoughts
While Walking the Dog

Stories

by
Lynn Ruth Miller

excentrix press
Street Saint Publications
Pacifica, CA 94044

Published by:
(excentrix press)
441 Brighton Road
Pacifica, CA 94044
ISBN 1-931090-97-1

Cover Design and Layout
by Barbera / Arnaudie Design Group

Photography
by Rod Searcy

Dedicated to Chris Hunter
with love and appreciation
For loving these stories as I do
and giving them their readers.

The characters in THOUGHTS WHILE WALKING THE DOG are products of the author's imagination and although many of them have names of people the author has known, they bear no relation to real people. These incidents are often based on fact but have been embellished far beyond truth.

In Appreciation

This collection of stories would never have happened without the encouragement and loving care they received from the Barbera / Arnaudie Design Group who organized, edited and formatted them into a work of art.

My thanks as well to Nancy Merchant who checked each story for spelling and grammatical errors. She has become the fairy godmother of my writing and a blessing to all of us involved in the production of my work.

Another thank you goes to Mary Kingland who has always kept my spirits up and my nose to the proper grindstone. It is she who helped with the final selection of tales in this volume and kept me laughing through the process.

A last note of thanks to the people of Pacifica who read many of my stories first as columns in The Pacifica Tribune and wrote letters of encouragement, praise and love to the author.

A chord of recognition must sound for Elaine Larsen who has always believed in my work and encouraged me with all the love and enthusiasm in her heart. I am grateful.

The most credit for the birth of these fantasies belong to Stephanie and Esther Schnauzer, Amy P. Yorkie, Dorothy Mutt, Paul Chihuahua and tiny Donald Poodle who have been my ever loyal companions on these walks and the catalyst to the thoughts that spring to my mind as I monitor their habits and observe their unquenchable joie de vivre.

And a note of encouragement to all of you who have outrageous thoughts while doing something else. May my example encourage you to preserve those ideas in writing. They will give you immortality.

- Lynn Ruth Miller

Table of Contents

- - -

On Knowing Lynn Ruth Miller

I'm not a writer. Oh, I always say I want to be a writer, and I've been making my living as a journalist for nearly the past two decades, but I'm still not a real "writer."

On the other hand, Lynn Ruth Miller is a writer. She lives and breathes to write, to create and to make a mark in the world. She is an inspiration to people who harbor the dream of being a writer or an artist, of overcoming personal obstacles and starting an actual writing career.

Being one of those people myself, I was interested in writing a feature story about a tiny little woman in Pacifica who said she was working on a novel. A journalist has the sometimes odd duty of telling other people's stories, hoping they will be interesting rather than enervating to readers. Stories about people who want to be writers can be deadly dull, so there has to be a news hook, an angle, something different.

As soon as I met Lynn Ruth Miller, I knew that the news hook would be the dynamic life force of this tiny woman who had suffered emotional battering throughout her life. Rather than giving up and feeling that her life had not been what she wanted, Lynn Ruth Miller decided that it's never too late to have the life you want.

She and I became friends after that initial article about her struggles to publish her novels. The recognition the Pacifica Tribune gave to her in her own community turned out to be a happy generator of support for her. She capitalized on her newfound celebrity, so to speak, and embarked on nearly a decade of growth, creativity and happiness that rubs off on everyone she knows.

Giving her an immediate audience for her humorous outlook on life, particularly her own, the Pacifica Tribune showcased Lynn Ruth Miller's columns. She named the column "Thoughts While Walking the Dog," and refused to let me put her picture above each column; instead she wanted her dog's face there. The column's literary, often longer-than-usual personal style is not something most small newspapers would normally publish, but readers responded positively and Lynn Ruth Miller continued to write them.

Although she often thanks the Pacifica Tribune for giving her a platform from which to launch her many successes, I must say that Lynn Ruth Miller is more inspirational to me than I could ever be to her. My success was simply in recognizing her special qualities.

Life is fleeting and art is also fleeting. What Lynn Ruth Miller shows every day of her existence is that art can enhance life, both for the creator and the audience. And, perhaps more importantly, that it's never too late to follow your dream. To capture even a drop of the powerful energy that is Lynn Ruth Miller's life force would be enough to make writers and artists of us all.

Chris Hunter
Publisher
The Pacifica Tribune
March 16, 2001

The Policeman is My Friend . . . Usually

I entertain a love/hate relationship with the police department. Put an otherwise reasonable officer on traffic control and he is transformed into an angry beast. Any patrolman who stops my car reminds me of my first husband when he discovered I had driven two miles on a broken axle. How could you be so stupid?" he roared.

"You told me not to be late, honey," I replied.

My husband divorced me immediately.

California police do not have to divorce me. They issue tickets, which is far more painful. I will never forget the tirade I received when an officer saw me making a U turn under the sign that said NO U TURN. "WHAT were you trying to do?" he thundered.

"Read that sign," I explained.

That cost me $75 and I only escaped traffic school by being unbelievably obedient for the next three years.

Then there was the time I was singing along with Perry Como as I drove north on 280. "I loved you as I luh-hu-hoved you. . ." I crooned.

I was just about to really hit that high note when I noticed a police car signaling me to pull over to the side of the road. A very young policeman marched to my open window. "Have you been drinking?" he asked.

"I was singing," I said.

"You were swerving all over the highway, Madame. Let me see your license."

I blushed. "It was my favorite song," I explained.

This communication problem never happens with policewomen. I had my three dogs in the car when I heard a suspicious choking sound. I glanced in the rear view mirror to see my youngest barfing into my groceries. A very sweet lady stopped my car. "Did you know you were going seventy-five?" she asked.

She flashed her light into the back seat of the car. "My dear!" she said. "You do have a problem. If you don't hurry, you'll have to throw out all those packages. It's soaking in."

She patted my hand and I accelerated. We understood each other and why not? We were both women, after all.

Now, when a male officer makes a house call, he is instantly transformed from an angry chauvinist into a charming gentleman. He is chivalrous and polite, soft spoken and kind. In fact, he reminds me of my father. Each time one of those darling young men come to my door, I am convinced that the adage I learned in kindergarten is absolutely true: The Policeman is my Friend.

One officer chided me for setting fire to my back fence when I attempted to add fireplace ashes to my azaleas. The nicest fellow explained that the poor girl in a short skirt who was stopping all those cars was not lost. "She's a hooker, Miss Miller," he said.

I am a very short woman and I tend to cook dinner when my neighbors are asleep. When the light bulb in my kitchen goes, I cannot reach the ceiling fixture and I cannot wake my neighbors. Instead, I call the only friend I know who is awake in the wee morning hours: the police. Officers from Massachusetts to Redwood City have never failed me. However, when I tried this request in Pacifica, the sergeant who answered the telephone sounded as if he had just issued thirty traffic tickets not to mention the dozens of schnooks he had caught with unbuckled seat belts." Do you mean to tell me you want me to squander taxpayer's money to drive over to your house to CHANGE A LIGHT BULB?" he shouted.

I cleared my throat and smiled into the telephone. I understand angry men and I know how to deal with them. "I wouldn't dream of doing such a thing," I assured him. "If you're too busy to help me, I'll call the fire department. They won't mind helping me. They are lovely boys."

There was a long pause. "I get off duty in twenty minutes," he said. "Can you wait that long?"

"Of course," I said.

See what I mean? Our police force is paternal to a man.

About four years ago, a girl named Charmain had to give up her new kitten. I offered to adopt him and I named him Fred. I should have known that any favor from a person named after a roll of toilet paper would have something unsavory about it. Sure enough, one year later, Charmain kidnapped Fred and took him to her new pets allowed apartment.

I was outraged. Fred was part of my family! Blinded by tears, I called the one telephone number I knew would help. The police station. The dispatcher immediately sent out a young men who had obviously spent the entire day dealing with choked expressways and four car collisions. He listened to my problem with an iced expression while my tears dripped on the threshold and splashed on his polished shoes. "This is not a matter for the police," he said. "Why don't you take the woman to small claims court?"

Now I was shocked. "If you had been kidnapped, young man, would money have taken your place in your mother's heart?"

His hesitation told me all I needed to know. He was the product of a dysfunctional family and didn't understand the maternal drive. I paused to control my grief and then raised my chin as regally as I could with my nose dripping and my eyes swollen shut. "I do not want cash, young man," I said. "I WANT FRED."

When this obtuse fellow left, I called the police department once more. Since this is a family newspaper, I will not repeat what I told the dispatcher." Isn't there someone there who loves animals?" I asked.

"There certainly is," she said. "And I will have him call you right now."

The captain who telephoned me was a prince. He listened to my tale of intrigue and abduction and he said, "Give me Charmain's telephone number. "I can't promise you anything, but sometimes a word in the right place does wonders."

I do not know what that word was. I only know that Fred was romping in my yard within the hour.

That captain who said the magic word is now the chief of police in my town. Obviously someone besides me knows a good man when they see one. And it is a great relief to me that the man in charge of my safety is nothing like any of the men I have married. He is a man who reminds me very much of my father.

A Warning to Young Men

A friend of mine who lives in a rambunctious neighborhood in Chicago named her cat, Malcolm. "When I come home late at night, I shout, 'I'm home, Malcolm!' and I feel very secure," she explained. "I know that anyone lurking in a dark alley will think someone is in the house to protect me."

I do not name my animals human names for protection. My pets are my children and I would no more call Amy, "Fido" than my mother would have christened me "Spot". Sometimes this naming habit of mine creates very confusing situations and the incident that stands out in my mind happened when my family consisted of David, a dog tortured by fleas; Cindy, a poodle with body odor so potent I was aware of her presence when I pulled the car into the garage; Eileen, a cat with a malevolent attitude and Sarah, a kitten with a bent for projectile vomiting. I decided that a visit to my family vet might be in order to solve some of these problems.

I asked my seven year old neighbor Mark to help me get the animals in the car to take them for their check ups. I needed help because David's constant scratching propelled him all over the car, Eileen despised cages and could chew through their metal bars before I got down the drive, and you know what Sarah did the minute she was confined. Cindy was an especially affectionate little dog. She liked to sit on my lap while I drove and fasten her eyes to mine. When she rested her paws on my shoulders and gazed adoringly at me, I understood how it felt to be in the gas chamber.

The vet's name was Harold Harter. He was so far past the accepted retirement age that he had trouble remembering his name but he insisted he knew his business. His wife Gladys was very sharp and she was his receptionist. His assistant was his son, Young Harold, fresh out of veterinary college, his head filled with advanced technology.

Mark and I managed to herd the four animals into the office and Gladys nodded her greeting. "We are ready for you!" she said. "Harold! The Miller pets are here!"

She ushered us into the examining room and began to recite everybody's symptoms. The doctor cut her short. "I can handle this Gladys," he said. "You go answer the telephone."

He smiled at me and I shook his hand. "This is Mark, doctor, "I shouted. "He came along to help me."

The doctor nodded and picked up Sarah. "What's wrong with this one?" he asked.

Sarah threw up on his sleeve and he nodded to Young Harold. "Better take its temperature, son," he said.

Young Harold nodded and lifted Sarah's tail. He inserted the thermometer and Sarah barfed on his shoe. Dr. Harter directed his attention to David. David was attacking his vermin with such animation that he created a small tornado of air in the room. "Poor fella," he said. "We have a new serum that might help him. Just lift Mark up on the table and I will give him a shot."

Mark took my hand and his eyes filled with tears." I hate shots," he whispered.

I picked up my vibrating puppy and put him on the examining table. "You mean DAVID," I explained.

Dr. Harter gave David his medication and handed him to me. He looked at Cindy. It was warm in that room and Cindy panted as if she were on the desert. Her problem was unmistakable. The doctor inhaled and coughed. "Whew!" he said.

He lifted up my poodle's lips and examined her mouth. When he came up for air, his face was a strange shade of purple. "Needs her teeth cleaned," he gasped. "You'll have to leave her here overnight."

He nodded to Eileen. "What's wrong with HER?" he said.

Eileen hissed. The doctor reached down to lift her and she tore his lab coat into streamers. "She has a bad disposition," I explained. "I think something is hurting her."

The doctor nodded. "I'll give her an antibiotic," he said. "There's a virus going around."

Suddenly, we heard a loud clink. All of us turned to stare at Sarah. Somehow, she had managed to expel the thermometer inside her and it landed on the tile floor. Young Harold grabbed it and read the result. "My God, Dad!" he said. "This cat is SICK!"

I looked at Sarah and I too became concerned. "Her eyes are crossed!" I exclaimed.

The doctor shook his head. "That wouldn't give her digestive problems," he said. "She must have the same virus the other one has."

"But her eyes were fine when I brought her in here," I said.

"No they weren't," said the doctor. "You just didn't notice them. I could cut the optic nerve if it bothers you."

"I don't think that will be necessary," I said and began to gather my animals together to take them home. Eileen was flat out on the floor, David was gnawing at a flea so large it would have dwarfed a gorged mosquito and

Sarah? Well, poor Sarah couldn't seem to walk in a straight line. The doctor glanced at the handful of charts in his hand. "If you put Mark up here, " he said. "I'll give him that rabies shot."

Mark fled out the door. "Wait in the car, honey," I called. "I'll be right there."

When I got to the car, Mark helped me get my pets inside the vehicle. "Would you like to come back with me tomorrow to pick up Cindy?" I asked.

He shook his head. "I'm afraid," he said. "What if he makes my eyes cross, too?"

I put my arms around him. "Nonsense," I said. "Just remember to keep your pants buckled up tight and you'll have nothing to worry about."

That incident happened many years ago, but I don't believe I have ever given a young man better advice. I offer it now as a gift to all my male readers: If you want to see things clearly and stay out of trouble, always keep your pants buckled up good and tight.

Almost anything is easier
to get into than to get out of.
- Agnes Allen

The Melting Pot

Children need models more than critics.
- Joubert

My mother's family came to Toledo, Ohio from Yasse, Rumania in 1900. My grandma had lived in a hut with a dirt floor and you can imagine how thrilled she was when my grandpa presented her with the white frame house he had built for her. It had wooden floors, a big front porch with a glider and a real icebox in the kitchen. My grandma bought her groceries in shops run by immigrants like herself and spent the rest of the day keeping house. She spoke Yiddish and that's the language my mother learned.

When my mama entered kindergarten, my grandma bundled her into thick woolen underwear that rumpled around her ankles and a loose dress with a bow at the back. Her hair was combed into long curls tied with a huge ribbon. She smiled at her new teacher and greeted her in Yiddish.

In those days, teachers made no effort to understand the language of the immigrant children who entered their classrooms. It was the child's responsibility to speak the national language. No one encouraged my mother to be proud of her ethnic heritage. Instead, she felt ignorant and confused. And so the worst happened. My mother flunked kindergarten.

Her shame was immense. Somehow, she managed to master the language enough to pass the first grade and by the time she was a teenager, she dressed like everyone else in her class and there wasn't a trace of the old country in her words. Still, she was humiliated by the different way her family lived and the strange foods they ate. She swore that when she had a child, that child would look like children in the magazines she read and it would speak faultless English. It would eat the American Way. No spicy Eastern European stews drenched in chicken fat and reeking of garlic. Her child would go to bed at seven and lunch on tuna fish and mayonnaise, because she was American.

I was that child.

My mother dressed me in starched Shirley Temple dresses and polished Mary Jane shoes. I wore slender leggings and a fitted navy blue coat with a white velvet collar to protect me from the elements.

The finishing touch to my outfit was a classy little hat with a white feather that bobbed as I walked. . . a far cry from rumpled woolen underwear and that shapeless dress that hung in uneven lengths somewhere in the vicinity of my mother's knees.

I drank orange juice for breakfast and finished my homogenized milk at every meal. I ate my salads on a separate plate and could not touch dessert until I finished my vegetables. I was not allowed to lisp or slur my words. I never heard baby talk and I certainly never heard Yiddish . . .except at my grandma's house.

When I was three years old, my parents took a month's vacation in Miami Beach. They left me with my grandma. I adored my bubbie. That was what I called her in my perfect American diction. She called me Leenie Root.

The minute my Mama kissed me good by, my grandmother took me into the house and opened up the trunk where she kept my mother's old clothes. She swaddled me in my mother's woolen underwear and topped it with a pink, shapeless dress that had patches at the elbow and hole right near the hem. I thought it was beautiful because it smelled like my bubbie to me. My grandma folded up my Shirley Temple dress and wrapped it in mothballs. "It's too cold to wear such a t'ing in vinter," she said. "Now, come. I will comb your hair."

She stood me on a chair next to the sink and formed long curls on my head with a wet comb. She tied them back with a great big ribbon and showed me my reflection in her hand mirror. I was thrilled. I looked just like the picture on the mantle of my mama and all my aunts.

How can I ever describe the magic of that month? I woke up each morning to a breakfast of hot oatmeal smothered in sweet butter and syrup and then downed a large cup of baby coffee (1% coffee, 99% milk.) At lunch I ate corned beef or pickled herring with raw onions. I smelled just like my mama did before she left home and learned about halitosis.

Every afternoon, my grandma told me stories about my mama and her three sisters. After dinner, she scooped me up on her lap and we practiced a special American surprise for my mother.

On the day my parents returned, Mama ran up the steps of her childhood home with her arms outspread. "Lynnie!" she cried.

I looked at the tanned stranger who smelled of expensive perfume and I shrunk behind by bubbie's skirt. "Who's dat?" I whispered.

My mother looked at me and tried to hide her horror. I stood before her, my rumpled underwear sagging around my ankles, my muslin dress stained with mustard and hot pastrami. My hair was pulled back in long curls. I smelled like a delicatessen and I looked exactly like she did when she was that tormented child frightened by a hostile, new world.

My grandma patted me on the cheek and said. "Sing, Leenie Root.

Sing for you mama."

I knew exactly what to do. Hadn't we rehearsed this little routine every evening for a month? I threw back my shoulders, opened my mouth wide and I sang: "Yankee Tootle vent towndown, a ridin' on da po-o-ony!"

And my mother wept. "Oh, Mama" she cried. "How could you do such a thing?"

My grandma lifted me into the air and kissed both my cheeks. "Dat vas gorgeous, Leenie Root," she exclaimed and I can imagine the look she gave my mother over the top of my head. "You sang chust like Jeannette MacDonald!"

Today, we know something my own mother never understood. We know that America is richer for its variety. We don't hold a child back because he can't speak understandable English. Instead, we have special teachers to help that child communicate with others and I think that's a very good thing.

I am very proud of the progress women have made in this century, but I sometimes wonder at the price we paid. My grandma was an uneducated housewife who couldn't read and never dreamed of a life outside her home, but she was never too busy to love a child. Growing up can be a very frightening thing and it is reassuring indeed to know that, no matter how life batters you, in one beloved heart, you are always a treasure.

There is always one moment in childhood
When the door opens and lets the future in.
- Graham Greene

Thanksgiving from Scratch

If my aunt hadn't brought me those cranberry plants from Maine, I never would have done it. "I brought you a rare treat, she said. "These are the kind of cranberries we used to cook for our Thanksgiving dinner when I was a girl."

"Can't you buy the same thing nowadays in a supermarket?" I asked.

"You certainly cannot!" my aunt said. "Those bagged pellets aren't cranberries. They're cardboard imitations; no taste at all. You can't buy old fashioned flavor, my dear.

"Our Thanksgiving dinner tasted like real food. The meal served these days is nothing but a flat, flavorless substitute that costs twice as much. You don't know what a Thanksgiving feast is all about unless you do it the way my grandma did. Why, when I was a girl, it took all year to prepare for Thanksgiving because we grew our fixings. You could, do Thanksgiving the right way if you wanted to, you know. You have this nice old farm with plenty of room for wheat and corn. You have that barn out back and a chicken coop, the plum tree, apple trees and some rhubarb growing by the fence.

"But I know you! Lazy! You'd throw in the sponge before you got halfway there and settle for cooking up a lot of packaged groceries."

"I would not," I said. "I don't throw in sponges."

I was so indignant, I did not use my head. "All right, all right," I snapped. "I'll show you. I'll have your kind of Thanksgiving this year. It's only April. I have plenty of time."

"Wrong!" said my aunt. "If you start right now, you might. . . just might, mind you . . . be ready a year from next November."

"You're kidding," I said. "It couldn't take that long to make a dinner. What on earth do I have to do?"

"Well, first of all, you better dig a bog out back for those cranberries and pray you'll have enough in two years for a cupful of cranberry sauce."

That's how it all began. I lived out on a small farm with my three cats, my dog and a lot of peace and quiet. Once I began my preparations, I said good by to the peace and quiet for the next eighteen months. The cats and dog remained.

That spring, I dug the cranberry bog and planted wheat and corn to feed the livestock I would need for the Big Day. I plowed and dug and hauled until my muscles screamed halt. When I was too weak to move, I read books on the proper care of my livestock.

I bought one tom turkey and two turkey hens just in case one hen didn't appeal to the gobbler or didn't want to hatch her eggs. I named my new feathered friends, Dick, Jane and Sally. I bought a cow, too and I named her Spot. By the time I mastered milking her and churning butter, I felt like a true old-fashioned housewife with all the trimmings: backaches, calloused hands and water on the knee.

Turkeys are delicate creatures and I worried about them night and day. One cloud in the sky and I dashed out to the corn field where Dick, Jane and Sally were dining and rushed them back to their dry, clean nests. If they caught cold and dropped dead, I'd have to put off my dinner at least another year. I wasn't sure I'd survive that long.

Right around Christmas, Jane began to walk around the yard with a look of fulfillment, her head in the clouds. By New Year's Eve, I noticed Dick looked tired all the time. He could barely get up a good morning gobble. Sally strutted by him provocatively, shamelessly swinging her feathered tail.

I knew there would be eggs before long.

It was a busy winter. Every day, I prepared the soil in my fields, worked in the barn and turned the soil in the poultry parks. The parks weren't play areas with swings and green grass. They were the places where poultry romp, scratch, make love and answer nature's other call.

In March, each hen laid three eggs which she sat on with all the love and concern of every expectant mother.

In April, I started hoeing my fields to prepare them for spring planting. And of course, there were chicken eggs to gather, the cow to milk and three turkeys to keep dry and happy. In May, the little turkeys hatched six darling chicks. I shuddered to realize I would be eating three for my Big Feast and breeding three for the next year, if I lived through this one. I had to watch my victims very carefully. They couldn't go outside for at least five months. They had to be fed and kept clean and warm. A sudden frost would kill them; and if they got wet, Thanksgiving dinner would not be served.

Right after I got all my seeds planted, we had a violent rainstorm. As the rain washed away the seeds, I galloped out to the field to coax Dick, Jane, Sally and their chicks out of the rain. The dog went after Spot. We all returned to the house soaking wet. I didn't bother changing clothes. I had to go right back out to gather the eggs and milk the cow.

All summer I worked in my fields and by September, I had a very creditable crop to harvest. Then, I began canning and preserving for the big day. I made pickles, jams, jellies and conserves. I even tried canning a few beans. I stored my onions, pumpkins, apples, carrots, cranberries and potatoes in the root cellar. I wrapped the cabbages in newspapers to store them and I dried the corn. After I harvested my wheat, I decided to add a special touch to my homemade Thanksgiving loaf. Anyone can buy flour to bake bread; the real treat is using your own wheat for the flour. Even my aunt's grandma didn't go to that extreme. I wrapped up a huge package of wheat and sent it parcel post to General Mills. I enclosed a letter telling them that I wanted to use my very own flour to bake bread for Thanksgiving. In about three weeks, I received a very tiny sack of flour with a letter wishing me a happy holiday.

Now, it was November. I called my family to let them know this was The Year for a Real Thanksgiving Dinner. I invited my aunt, her family, my parents and my sister. "Be here at two thirty," I said. "We'll eat at three."

I spent the next week washing linen and dishes. I polished my silver and crystal and made an old fashioned centerpiece of pumpkins, gourds and Indian corn for the table. That Wednesday, I was up at dawn baking my pies and bread. I refused to think about my afternoon chore.

I had to murder a turkey.

I walked out to the park, my hatchet concealed beneath my apron. There they all were, fluffy, fat and full of life. Tears filled my eyes. How could I face Jane and Sally? What would happen to their faith in mankind when the woman who had sheltered them and kept them dry for a year and a half slaughtered their fattest child? Well, it was too late now for tender sensibilities. I made a wild dash for Jane's eldest boy and grabbed for his neck. I ushered my victim to a secluded corner of the barn, clenched my teeth and chopped off his head. I dipped him in hot water to loosen the feathers and, before I knew it, I was looking at a naked fowl ready for the oven. I could hardly believe that, moments before, I was trying to keep his feet dry and his nest tidy. I offered up a quick prayer for forgiveness, muttered my heartfelt sympathy to Jane and took the bird into the house. I put it in the fruit room along with the butter. Then I washed the blood from my hands, but I couldn't rinse it from my heart. "Murderer!" I said to myself. "And what's even worse, you're going to eat the body. Even Bluebeard didn't do that. All he did was hang the corpses in the basement."

My heart was filled with shame but I had no time to mourn. I had to gather the eggs, milk the cow and spray soaps suds on my vegetables to wash the bugs away.

Thursday morning! I was up at five a.m. I gathered more eggs and milked Spot one more time. Dick, Jane and Sally were prowling around their park looking for their missing child. I averted my eyes and hurried into the kitchen to I prepare the deceased for the roasting pan. I stuffed him, coated him with lard and put him in the oven. My stove could barely hold the huge roasting pan, so I had to tie the door shut. Heat poured from the crack in the door, roasting the cats, the dog and me along with Jane's baby. "Serves you right," I muttered to myself.

I put the potatoes and corn to boil and skimmed some milk to get enough cream for whipping. I put the bowl, nestled in blocks of ice, upstairs in the bathtub. It was the only place I could think of that was out of the way. After I made the coleslaw, I sat down to polish some Jonathan apples to set out after the meal was over. I looked at the clock. It was two o'clock! Where had the morning gone? I rushed upstairs to take a bath. Just in time, I remembered the cream in the tub. I grabbed a bottle of cologne for a quick coverup and prayed that the mist wouldn't hit the cream. I put on a clean apron and went down to create the gravy.

"You can tell a good cook by her gravy," my aunt said. "If it has lumps in it, you don't have to bother with the rest of the meal."

I was determined that my gravy would be smooth as silk. I removed the bird from the pan and put flour and water in the drippings. I brought the whole thing to a boil and began to stir.

Lumps.

I stirred some more. I beat. I whipped. I cursed.

Lumps.

The doorbell rang. I left the gravy looking like brown tapioca and went to the door. There stood my mother and father and their pet canary. "I had to bring Caruso," my mother said. "He had diarrhea and he's molting. I was afraid he'd get depressed if I left him alone in the house."

My sister and her husband arrived at that moment with their three children and the dog. My aunt and her son, his wife and three children followed them into the house. "Smells pretty good," my aunt said.

I remembered the lumps in the gravy. I said nothing.

My sister, my mother and my aunt trooped into the kitchen to help me get everything on the table. I was dishing out food and giving instructions when I remembered. The potatoes! I forgot to mash the potatoes! The kitchen was so hot by then that the butter was melted and ready to pour. I threw it into the boiled potatoes with some of Spot's fresh milk and whipped them into a mountain of white fluff. I opened the windows, smoothed my hair and wiped my hands on my apron. The moment I had been slaving for was here. I took a deep breath and entered the dining room.

My table ordinarily seats six. There were fifteen of us. We sat squeezed shoulder to shoulder, the animals at our feet, the bird twittering from the chandelier.

Suddenly, it was quiet. My father asked the blessing and took up the carving tools. He sharpened the knife with a flourish and said, "Now, who wants white meat?"

My nephew spilled cranberry sauce on the tablecloth. My sister dragged her sleeve through the coleslaw. One cat jumped up on the table and knocked over three wine glasses . . . filled. The canary hit a high note and lost all his feathers. They floated into the gravy like a gentle mist from heaven.

Oh, blessed bird! The gravy was a mass of feathers and my reputation saved.

In less than twenty minutes, eighteen months of slave labor was demolished. All that was left were mountains of dirty dishes and bloated relatives. "Why don't the men and the children go into the other room while we clear the table?" my aunt said.

After the kitchen was clean, we all stood around the piano to sing Thanksgiving songs about over the river and through the woods and gathering together to ask the Lord's blessing. My brother-in-law sang bass, we sang the melody and the nude canary chirped the descant. Then my sister said, "I think we should all thank God for such a magnificent feast, don't you?" She turned to me. "And we thank you for preparing it for us. What are you thankful for?"

I didn't have to think about that one.

"Thank God it's over," I said.

"Amen to that," my aunt said. "And now, what are you going to do about Christmas?"

The Newcomer

But Lucifer and I
Still rage against the skies,
And weep - and weep for our
Remembered Paradise
- Lorenzo Sturkey

It was such a hot day. Her mother had dressed her in a brief, ruffled sunsuit, but she still felt moist and uncomfortable. Little ringlets of golden hair clung to her damp forehead. Her tiny face glistened, drenched in perspiration.

She felt restless . . . apprehensive. It wasn't only the heat. There was an air of restless expectation in the house. Her mother was preoccupied and distant . . . almost as if her mind were drifting away.

"Put your foot up on the chair, Susie, so I can buckle your shoe. I can't bend all the way down anymore," she said. "Be sure to be polite and don't cause trouble today, honey. It's awfully nice of Marsha's mother to take you to the zoo. We don't want her to be sorry she invited you, do we?"

"No, Mama. I'll be good; I promise. Can I feed the monkeys?"

The mother put her arms around the little girl and tried to hug away the fear that lurked behind the child's words. "Sure you can feed the monkeys. I'll give Aunt Eve money for popcorn. But don't you eat any. I don't want you to spoil your dinner.

She paused and chose her words carefully. "I may not be here when you come home, honey. If I'm gone, go upstairs and Aunt Rose will take care of you. Okay?"

"Will you have to go to the hospital today to get Neut?" the child asked.

"I think so."

"Can I listen to it kick?"

She put her head against her mother's distended belly. "I can feel it!" she said. "Oh, I just can't wait to see which it's going to be! I hope it's a Deborah instead of a David, don't you? A little sister would be so much fun!"

She glowed with her anticipation of a new playmate all her own, one who would never hit her or be nasty like some of the children on her street.

Suddenly, the insistent tattoo of an automobile horn tore the fabric of her fantasy. The mother wiped the child's damp forehead and kissed her. "There they are. Come on, Susie. I'll take you out to the car."

She clung to her mother's hand as they hurried out of the house. She tried to bite back her tears, but they shimmered behind her words. "I don't think I want to go to the zoo. It's too hot out. Let me stay home with you, Mama. Then I can be here when Neut comes. Please, Mama."

"Don't be silly, Susie. You've been talking about this trip all week. You love the animals. You know you do. Oh, honey, I don't know what I'm going to do with you. You can't be with me all the time."

"But I get scared without you, Mama."

The tears finally forced their way out of the corners of her eyes. Her lip quivered. It was always like that when she had to leave her mother. The only time she felt safe was when she was with her mama. She was so frightened when she went to school that at first her mother had to walk her there every morning and pick her up when kindergarten was over at noon. Her mama even sat in the back of the classroom that first week. Susie would turn around and wave whenever she got that awful knot in her stomach. Then she felt better and could hear what the teacher was saying again. It took a whole month before she was brave enough to let her mother stay at home. Then, Natalie took her to school instead and that was just fine.

She loved Natalie. She hoped her mother would bring home a little sister just like Natalie, only smaller, like her Shirley Temple doll. Then I'd have two of them, she thought. A big Natalie upstairs and a little one in my own house to play with all the time.

In school, she was always very quiet. She saw what happened to the children who made noise and she didn't want that to happen to her. The teacher's face would get all red and twisted and she would shout so loud that it hurt Susie's ears.

Her mother never screamed like that. She never twisted her face to make it ugly, either. Her mother was prettier than a movie star. She had long, red hair that she let Susie brush. It glistened and sparkled like it had stars in it. Her mama's laugh was like tinkling bells that made Susie feel all warm and soft inside whenever she heard it. Best of all was the way her mother smelled: like all the flowers in the prettiest garden in the world.

Susie always felt very cuddled and safe with Mama . . . always. But now, she had to leave her to go away with Marsha and Aunt Eve. What if her mother was gone when she came home? What if the house was all dark and she had to stay in it alone? What would she do? Susie clung tighter to Mama's hand until, too soon, they arrived at the waiting car.

"Here she is, Eve," said her mother. "She's so shy. I'm a little worried about this afternoon. Better take her to the bathroom when you get there. She'll be afraid to ask. And don't let her eat anything. She gets stomach aches."

"Don't worry so much, Pam. As soon as we get started, she'll be just fine. She has to learn to be away from you, sometime. It's going to be awfully hard for her when you have to divide your attention between her and the baby. When will it arrive? From the looks of you, it's any minute."

"You're right. I've had a back ache all morning, just like I did before Susie was born. The doctor says I have to wait until the pains are pretty close together and that might be hours from now. I hope this one is easier than Susie's was. They say you forget the pain or you'd never have another baby; but I could never forget that kind of torture. I still have nightmares about it. That's why we waited so long before having this one. I was too frightened.

"My pains started in the afternoon with Susie, too. I can still remember that child slamming against my insides fighting to get out. But when I got to the hospital, I wouldn't dilate, even though I walked until I thought I'd drop. They didn't break my water until the next morning and then the pains were really unbearable; metal blocks slamming against my back. I pushed forever. . . at least it seemed like forever. It was the hardest work I ever did."

Her frown of reminiscence faded into a brilliant smile. "But oh was it worth it! Just look at the treasure I got! Susie has been perfection from the minute she arrived."

She leaned down and hugged the child to her. "Haven't you, angel?"

"Haven't I what, Mama?"

"Haven't you been my little sunshine your whole sweet life? That's why I'm going to give you a little baby to play with. So I can say, `Thank you, my darling Susie, for being you!'"

"I love you, Mama."

Susie clung tight to her mother and nuzzled her face in her skirt.

Eve laughed. "Hey, you two. Cut the love scene. Listen, Pam, who's dependent on whom around here? It seems to me you're as lost without Susie as she is without you."

"You're right, I guess. But I became so attached to her after Phil left me. Thank God I had you and Rose to live through that nightmare with me. I would have really fallen apart if it hadn't been for the two of you and Susie to love. She wasn't even three months old when he walked out, remember? If it hadn't been for Sam, we would have starved. I'll always believe Sam was the one who made Phil come home, but he denies it."

"I remember that homecoming," Eve said. "We were playing bridge while the two little girls napped. Susie must have been a year old by then .

. . and in he walked. Not a word of explanation. Just, `Hi, honey. Don't let me disturb your game. What's for dinner?"

"You know, he never did explain where he went or why. And I didn't ask him. I was petrified he'd turn around and walk back out the door. Sam couldn't support us forever. There are limits to what you'll do for someone, even if he is your baby brother.

"And I'm still scared he'll leave me again. What would I do? I'm all alone here and I could never get a job. I was so in love with Phil, I couldn't wait to finish high school to marry him. And this depression has made it impossible even for skilled people to find work.

"And now, they're talking about war. It's no time to be saddled with two kids and no breadwinner."

"You'd be surprised how well you'd manage, Pam," said Eve. "The trouble with you is that you're afraid to try. No wonder Susie is always afraid of new things! She takes after you."

"I know she does and I feel awful about it. What a terrible legacy to give a child. Children are so sensitive. I've tried to hide my uncertainties from Susie, but she senses them, I know she does."

She put her hand on her friend's arm and she sighed. "You know something, Eve? Sometimes, I think I'd be better off without Phil. Poorer, perhaps, but a lot happier. Our relationship hasn't been much since he came back. I feed him and keep the house clean and Susie quiet. I guess I'm afraid to love him again. Can you blame me? I know it sounds ridiculous, but the pain of his walking out on me was a lot worse than the pain of having Susie.

"Look at the time! We'll talk away the afternoon! You won't get to the zoo and I'll drop this baby right in the middle of the street. I told Rose you're taking Susie to the zoo today just in case I do have to leave for the hospital before you get back. She said to tell you to bring Susie upstairs. She and Natalie will watch her if I'm not home."

"Don't worry about it, Pam. Everything will be fine. We're going to have a wonderful time, aren't we, Susie?"

The child nodded her head, but she gripped her mother's skirt still and her eyes were dark holes of apprehension. A tear glistened on her cheek. Her mother lifted her into the car and shut the door. She reached in the window and took her daughter's damp, worried face in her hands. "Be good, Susie. Remember, if I'm not home, go right upstairs to Aunt Rose. She'll be waiting for you."

She kissed the child. "What an angel you are. I love you lots and lots."

"I love you, too, Mama," said Susie and she waved good bye.

She stared out the car window until her mother was out of sight. Then she folded her hands together and held them tight as if their strength would hold back her fears.

All the time they were at the zoo, the child was silent. She didn't want Marsha's mother to shout or make her face all ugly the way the teacher at school did when someone made too much noise or was naughty. She couldn't wait for the afternoon to end. She wanted to go back home. She didn't have to be so careful at home. No one ever screamed at her there. If she did something wrong and her daddy was home, he always yelled at her mother, not her. Then her mama explained the right way to act. It wasn't scary at all. Except she hated the loud sounds her father made even though he wasn't speaking to her.

At last the day was over and Aunt Eve's car pulled into Susie's familiar driveway. "Thank you very much, Aunt Eve," she said. "Good bye, Marsha. I had a very good time."

She ran up to the house as fast as she could. When she got to the door, it was locked.

"Mama!" she called. Her voice had a sharp edge of hysteria and she shivered despite the heavy summer heat. "Mama! Where are you?"

She could feel the fright rising in her body, flooding her. She could hardly breathe and her throat tightened up so that no sound would come out. She beat hard on the door.

"Is that you, Susie?"

She looked up through tears of anguish. Aunt Rose was leaning out the window. "Your mother went to the hospital, honey. Natalie will be right down to bring you upstairs. Okay?"

A moment later, Natalie came bounding down the back steps. "Come on, punkin. Let's go upstairs and I'll read you a super-duper story about a little girl who lost her shoe at a dance. Would you like that?"

"Oh, yes! Yes, yes, yes."

The fear was gone now; gone because Natalie was there and she felt safe once more. Natalie took her hand and they trudged up the steps together. Oh, it was wonderful when she was with Natalie; almost as nice as being with her mother. Natalie was really big. She was only going to be at Susie's school one more year before she went to a bigger one. "Then, who will walk me to school?" Susie asked.

"Why, you'll be big enough to go all by yourself by that time," Natalie said.

"I'll be scared all alone," said Susie.

She was never scared when she was with Natalie. Natalie wouldn't let dogs bite her or big boys hit her; and Natalie didn't ever scream and twist up her face or get angry at anything. When her face twisted up, it was because she was laughing . . . and she did that all the time. It sounded like beautiful music to Susie, as pretty as her mother's laugh, but different. Natalie was laughing now as they climbed the stairs. Oh, I hope mama brings home a teeny tiny Natalie! Susie thought.

Aunt Rose was waiting at the door. "Your mother went to the hospital just about an hour ago, Susie. We'll know pretty soon if you have a sister or a brother. Go to the bathroom and wash your hands, now, honey. I have dinner ready . . . all your favorite things" Hamburgers with mustard and chocolate pudding! Doesn't that sound good?"

"Yes, Aunt Rose. Is Daddy coming up here, too?"

"Later, Susie. Right now, he's at the office. We'll eat supper without him."

"Sure," said Susie. "Mama and I never wait for him either. He usually comes home right before I go to bed."

It was fun at Aunt Rose's, but very strange. Nothing smelled right. The rooms had a different odor, more like Uncle Harry's cigar smoke; and Aunt Rose smelled like different flowers than her mother. She liked her mother's flower smell better.

Even the food was different. The hamburgers looked the same as the ones her mother made, but these had funny little things in them and Aunt Rose didn't cook onions to put over them. Susie had to sit on a pillow to reach the table and it made her feel awkward. What if she spilled the milk?

Besides, it was hard to concentrate on eating when she missed her mother so much. Nothing ever seemed right without her mama. Susie hoped she'd hurry home from the hospital, but Aunt Rose said her mother would be gone a week. That was a very long time.

It was time to go to bed before her father came upstairs to Aunt Rose's, but Susie was used to that. She never saw much of her daddy. He was always too busy to talk to her or to her mother either. Susie had a vague suspicion that her mother didn't like her father very much. But she loves me, Susie thought. Wouldn't it be nice if Daddy went on a long vacation? Then, I wouldn't have to be so quiet when he comes home and Mama wouldn't stop laughing the way she does when he walks into the house. He's always so growley and gets so mad when I talk too much. I wonder if he'll make Aunt Rose and Natalie stop smiling when he gets here the way he does with Mama and me?

"Bedtime, Susie!" called Natalie. "Hurry, so we'll have time for that story!"

Susie hurried. She scrambled into her pajamas and jumped into the strange bed in Natalie's room. Natalie pulled the covers up to the child's chin and tucked her in good and tight. Mama had sent up her teddy bear and her Shirley Temple doll to sleep with but it still wasn't as nice as being in her own bed at home. These sheets had blue flowers on them and they felt very cold.

The story was a good one. Susie loved how the prince found Cinderella and made her into a princess. It sounded very exciting and Susie wished someday she could be a princess, too. When the story was over and Natalie assured her that everyone in it lived happily ever after, the two of them blew out the light and Natalie sat right next to the bed and held her hand until Susie fell asleep.

The next morning, Aunt Rose came into the bedroom and said, "Guess what? Your mother got you a sister!"

Susie sat up in bed. Her excitement was so big she thought she'd explode. "A Deborah!" she said. "Just what I wanted! When can I see her? Now?"

Aunt Rose laughed. "Not this minute, but pretty soon. We'll go to the hospital just as soon as I get the house cleaned up."

It took a long time for Aunt Rose to get all her work done. Before she finished, it was lunch time. Right after lunch all three of them went to the hospital.

Susie had never been in a hospital before except the time her mother went to get her and she didn't remember that. Everything in the building looked so big. There were lots of serious looking people standing around the whole place smelled like the alcohol her mother used to clean the thermometer before she took Susie's temperature. When Aunt Rose and Natalie took her into the elevator, Susie felt smothered. Everyone pushed her together and she couldn't see anything. She couldn't move either and one big man stepped right on her toe. Susie clung to Natalie's hand.

It seemed like forever before Natalie said,"Come on, punkin. This is our floor."

Everyone in the elevator crowded to the side to let them out. There were lots of ladies in white dresses walking around the floor. Their foot steps made loud, clicking sounds. It smelled funny there, too like after her mother had washed the floors at home.

"Now, you walk between us so no one will notice you, Susie," said Aunt Rose. "They don't usually allow little children up here but your mother has a private room and we just might get away with bringing you here. Quick, now!"

As she walked down the long hall with Aunt Rose and Natalie, Susie was partly hidden by their long coats and the packages they carried. No one even looked at them and at last, they reached her mother's room where Susie was safe.

Her mother was sitting in a great big high bed and Susie could hardly see her. She held a large, bumpy looking blanket to her chest. Susie ran to the bed and held her face up for a kiss, but her mother didn't lean over. She stayed very still and said, "Careful, Susie. Don't jiggle the bed. I'm feeding Deborah."

"Where is she?" Susie asked.

She hadn't seen a baby anywhere.

Her mother turned the bundle she was holding around. "Right here," she said.

Susie looked. Sure enough, right in the middle of all those blanket folds was a red ugly face with black hair. Right now, the face was all scrunched up and it was screaming. Susie put her hands over her ears. She was stunned. That awful looking thing couldn't be Deborah! She didn't look like Natalie or her Shirley Temple doll or anything nice at all. She looked more like the monkeys she and Marsha saw yesterday and her face was all twisted up like the teacher's when she got angry.

"Isn't she pretty?" said her mother.

She held the screaming bundle to her shoulder and patted it. Susie could see some white stuff come out of the little red mouth and it smelled sour. "She needed to burp," said her mother. "Do you want to kiss her?"

She put the baby close to Susie's face. The smell was awful and the baby's face started getting red and twisted up again. "No!" said Susie. "I don't like her! She makes noises and she smells! She's . . she's ugly!"

The child turned away from the bed and ran out of the room down the endless corridor . . . faster and faster . . . away from the screaming, smelly bundle, away from this terrible place where her mother didn't act right . . . away, away, away. Her feet pounded on the tiled floor. CLICK, click, click, CLICK, click, click. Her footsteps echoed from wall to wall and chased her as she ran away to anywhere, anywhere but this cold, white hospital with it's antiseptic smells and strange, busy people.

At last, crying and out of breath, she stopped. She sat down on the floor and let all the tears come pouring down her face.

And then Natalie was there wiping her face and hugging her. "It's all right, punkin. Really, it is. Let's go back and say good bye to your mother and the baby. We can come see them again, tomorrow."

"NO," sobbed the child. "I don't want to see that thing ever again. Ever! Tell Mama to throw it away and come home right away.!"

Natalie half dragged, half carried the child back to the hospital room. Her mother still had that bundle in her arms. She was frowning at Susie. "Be a good girl, now, Susie and stop crying," she said. "I'm ashamed of you making all that racket and disturbing all the other mothers and their babies.

Why are you being such a naughty, nasty, girl? You'll get used to Deborah as soon as she gets home. You shouldn't say such terrible things about your baby sister.

"Just you remember, young lady, I got her because you begged for her so you better be nice to her. You hear me?"

Susie nodded. She was paralyzed with a brand new fear. What had happened to her mother when she came to this awful place. Had her real Mama vanished and this angry woman taken her place?

"Now, go home with Aunt Rose and stop making such a fuss," said the new, mean mama. "I hardly know you when you act this way!"

She turned to Aunt Rose. "I hope she hasn't been a lot of trouble, Rose. I know how hard it's been for you with Phil's irregular hours and all the extra things you've had to do. I can't tell you how much I appreciate it."

She held the new baby to her and rocked back and forth. Her face was serious and as hurt as the child's who stood at the foot of the bed. "You know, Phil hasn't even bothered to come here to see the baby," she continued. "He's called, of course, but he says he can't break away. His own daughter."

Susie could hear the tears in her mother's voice. Poor Mama. No wonder she was so strange. Something awful was hurting her.

"I can't believe that man's indifference," her mother said to Aunt Rose. "It's as if he serviced me because I wanted the baby for Susie and now he's washed his hands of the whole business. Some marriage I've got!"

"Oh, Pam, don't be so hard on him . . . or on yourself, either. Things will work out just fine. He'll probably be thrilled when he sees the baby. It's just that men have an aversion to hospitals. Besides, this is Phil's busy season at the office. Be thankful this was an easier birth than Susie's was. At least you won't have the bleeding and the backaches you had last time."

"Oh, you're right, I suppose, Rose. I should count my blessings . . . but the only one I see is Susie; and she is worth everything. This baby is a real screamer; colicky, won't sleep, always cranky. I don't know how to cope with her. The slightest thing will start her crying. I can't believe so much enraged sound could come out of such a tiny body. Remember how sweet Susie was? It was only her arrival that was such a killer. She was a rainbow from then on."

She turned to her little daughter. "Are you going to show Aunt Rose what a perfect little person you can be?" she asked.

"Sure I am, Mama," said Susie.

She smiled but she still felt uncertain. Now her mother sounded right, but the bed was so high up, Susie couldn't see her face to make sure.

"Can I kiss you good bye, Mama?" she asked.

"Not now, honey. Can't you see I'm holding Deborah? I'll blow you a kiss. That's just as good. I love you, Susie."

Now, Susie felt a little better. "I love you, too, Mama. When will you come home?"

"At the end of the week, honey. Now mind Aunt Rose and make me proud of you."

Susie nodded. "Yes, Mama. But I miss how you say goodnight and . . ." she bit her lip. . . "And everything."

The child buried her face in the covers and sobbed.

"Come on, precious," said Natalie. "It's time to take you home."

All the next week, Susie was very quiet. She refused to go to the hospital again. At night, her tears would start each time she remembered how funny her mother had acted when she held that ugly thing in the blankets.

"Why don't you make a picture to surprise your mother when she comes home?" asked Aunt Rose. "Natalie will help you."

"Okay," said Susie. "Do I have to make one for Deborah, too?"

"Why, I think that would be very nice," said Aunt Rose.

"Maybe if I make her a picture, she won't scream so loud," said Susie. "Maybe my present will make her smile. Does she know how to smile, yet or is she too little?"

Aunt Rose laughed. "Of course she's not too little to smile! You smiled the very first time I saw you in the hospital. Deborah is probably smiling at your mama right now."

Susie worked as hard as she could on both pictures. She collected bright flowers outdoors and pasted them along the bottom of the paper. She added a few leaves and a tin foil sun. She surrounded the sun with cotton batten clouds and drew in some trees and houses. On the back of each picture, she printed WELCOME HOME, and on her mother's picture, she added, I LOVE YOU XXXXOOOO, SUSIE."

Natalie said both pictures were beautiful. Aunt Rose liked them, too and so did Uncle Harry. Even Daddy said they were very nice. Natalie helped Susie wrap them in tissue paper. Susie pasted flowers on the outside of each package. She could almost hear her mother's tinkling laugh when Susie gave the presents to her. Susie just couldn't wait.

Finally, it was the end of the week. Aunt Rose went to the hospital to bring her mother and Deborah home. All that morning, Susie helped Aunt Rose clean the house. Then, they went to the grocery store to buy things for her mother to cook for supper. "Now, you play with Natalie until I get back with your mother and the baby," said Aunt Rose. "Then, you can give them your presents. Your mama will be very proud when I tell her how good you were, Susie."

Aunt Rose was gone such a long time. Susie watched at the window, her nose pressed to the glass. At last, the car pulled into the driveway and there was her mother with that bundle of blankets in her arms. Deborah was screaming, but Aunt Rose held her so Susie could kiss her mother hello. The child clung to the familiar coat and breathed the sweet scent that meant security and love to her. "Oh, I missed you so much!" she said.

Her mother stroked her head . "I missed you, too, honey. But now, we're all home together. Go inside now. I'm awfully tired and I need to quiet the baby and put her to bed. Then, we can talk. I want to hear all about what you've done while I've been away."

Susie ran upstairs to get the presents she had made and Aunt Rose went in the house with her mother. When Susie came into her own home downstairs, her mother was sitting at the kitchen table with Aunt Rose. Deborah was nowhere in sight and it was very still. "Where's the baby?" asked Susie.

"Shhh! She's sleeping on my bed," whispered her mother. "You can go see her if you're quiet. Don't wake her up, Susie."

Susie tiptoed into the bedroom still clutching the tissue wrapped packages. Deborah was on the bed and her face wasn't red and funny looking at all. She looked like a very serious doll. Her eyes were shut. Maybe if I kissed her, she'd smile, Susie thought.

The child started to climb on the bed to reach the baby's face. To her horror, the infant began to roll to the edge of the bed. Susie watched, paralyzed with fear as the baby and the blankets gathered momentum and tumbled to the floor. Deborah's eyes opened and her face got all red. She screamed so loud Susie's ears ached.

Her mother rushed into the room. "What have you done, you naughty little girl? Do you want to kill your sister? It took me forever to get her to sleep and now listen to her! You go outside this minute and don't come back until I call you!"

Susie stared at her mother. She was terrorized. She had never heard her mother scream like that. Was that really her own sweet mama, this woman whose face was twisted and ugly, whose voice was so harsh? Susie scuttled past her and ran for the door.

What had happened to her mother when she went to get Deborah? Why had she changed so much? Susie didn't like this new mother and she didn't like her new sister, either.

Oh, why weren't things the same as they were before? Home was an awful place now . . . just awful. She didn't feel safe there anymore, just scared.

She looked at the presents still clutched in her hands with their bright ribbons and yellow flowers. She took each one and tore it into little tiny pieces. The wind scattered them like snow in the bright afternoon sun, but Susie didn't see. Her eyes were blinded with tear

Human kind
Cannot bear very much reality.
- T. S. Eliot: BURNT NORTON

Dressing the Part

A little frippery goes a long way.
- Mademoiselle Bouffant

Whenever I go out on the town, I like to do it with panache. After all, if no one notices you when you walk through the door, why bother?

In the middle of my fifth decade of life, I realized that I was fast approaching my dotage and I was determined to convey the image of an elegant dowager rather than that of a wasted old hag. It would be a challenging task, given my paucity of raw materials, but I knew I could do it. All it took was a little advance planning.

I noted that most old ladies looked like clipped dogs when their hair began to thin and gray. Accordingly, I decided to let my hair grow long and adorn it with decorative paraphernalia to match my outfit. I dropped my hemlines to my ankles to conceal my bowing legs and the vivid splotches of color that made them resemble tubular Kandinsky paintings and launched the Draped Velvet Sparkling Satin phase of my attire.

It became my habit to top off my costumes with a matching feather boa wrapped around my ponytail. I thought the result was smashing and I certainly managed to raise a few eyebrows when I entered the room. When I exited in all my feathered finery, the place looked like the aftermath of a Technicolor performance of Swan Lake. My brilliant plumage floated into corners, added unwanted sparkle to dust mops and clogged vacuum cleaners for months after my departure.

These elaborate costumes became fond memory after the evening I was invited to the gala opening of a Gilbert and Sullivan Revue. I had decided that fuchsia was the ideal color to wear to redirect attention from the stage to the place I preferred it to be. I selected a pale pink gown with matching shoes and draped a fuchsia shawl around my shoulders. I decorated my ears with long dangling earrings and tied a fuchsia feather boa in my hair. I looked in the mirror expecting my usual rush of satisfaction when I saw the stunning result of my efforts, but instead of the glamorous image I expected, I saw an old lady who looked for all the world like a disoriented vulture caught in a windstorm.

My eyes filled with tears and my heart thumped wildly in my chest. I tore the feather boa from its clip, wrapped my hair in a geriatric bun and crept into the back row of the theater, unobtrusive as a pink shadow.

It was a disappointing evening and a revelation too shocking to absorb all at once. I had aged. The wrinkles and pouches in my face were those of an ancient crone. My skin was the color of a rotten lemon and its texture resembled a discarded sponge. To put it bluntly, I looked like hell.

I entered a hardware store not long after this depressing discovery and as the eager clerk rang up my purchases, he scrutinized my sagging jowls and exclaimed, "Whoops! I forgot your senior discount!"

The sign above the cash register said, "Ten per cent discount to all patrons over 65."

I looked at the boy bagging my hose nozzle and flood lights and couldn't decide whether to stab him in the heart or rush home and drink a tall, frosty glass of hemlock. It would be ten years before I reached 65 and he didn't even ask for my ID.

Now I know very well that true beauty resides in your heart and externals are so superficial that every intelligent person immediately ignores them. I firmly believe this WHEN I AM DISCUSSING SOMEONE ELSE. However, this was MY face, and it looked like a vintage tintype.

I called several plastic surgeons for help and the cost to disguise my drooping features was astronomical. Obviously, eternal youth is reserved for the affluent in our society. The senior poor must accept the ravages of age and live with a body whose parts gradually descend to their ankles as the years take their toll.

I had a dear friend from Japan who owned a coffee house down the street and I decided to share my grief and anger with her. She was the kind of person who meditated daily, did her yoga and tai chi religiously and lived in the Tao. If anyone could help me accept my fate, Toshimi could. I told her how defeated I felt in my attempt to age with a certain amount of aesthetic grace and she clasped her hands together under her chin and nodded, as Buddhists often do. “Leen,” she said. “Every age has a beauty all its own. The glow of youth would be most inappropriate on a face such as yours. You have grown far beyond the erratic swings of mood that characterize the young. Your beauty is in your wisdom.”

“Well it certainly isn’t in my face,” I said.

“But it is!” she said. “Your features reflects depth and understanding of a life well lived.”

I blushed. “Thank you,” I said.

“Would you like your espresso now?” she asked.

“Make it a double,” I said. “You’ve given me a lot to think about.”

She nodded wisely, as Buddhists do and I considered her words. “You are right, Toshimi,” I said. “When I was sixteen, I did not try to look like I was sixty. Why should I want to look like a teenager now that I have acquired all the privileges of age?"

"Exactly," said Toshimi. "Remember the anguish? Remember the uncertainty?"

I nodded. "I could never live through it all again. What a lovely philosophy you have! It must be very reassuring."

"Oh, it is," said Toshimi. "As long as I don't look in the mirror. Did you want cream?"

Growing old is like being penalized for
a crime you haven't committed
- Anthony Powell and my mother

The Gift My Mother Gave Me

I was a difficult birth and my mother had a great deal of trouble talking to me without resentment. I had caused her a lot of pain and besides, I couldn't carry on a decent conversation. When I was a few weeks old, a benevolent, gray haired lady knocked at our door and solved her dilemma. "I am Leona Mitchell," she said. "I represent MY BOOKHOUSE FOR CHILDREN. May I come in?"

She handed my mother a business card and followed her into the living room. She observed me with interest and tickled my chin. "How adorable!" she cooed.

"She's very demanding," said my mother. "I have to watch her every second."

"This child is like an iceberg," said Mrs. Mitchell. "The part you see is only a fraction of the entire person. You need to nourish her mind as well as her body if you want her to grow into a healthy, happy adult."

"Really?" said my mother. "I'd be happy if she'd just stop crying long enough to let me sleep through the night."

Mrs. Mitchell nodded. "That is why you should consider buying MY BOOKHOUSE FOR CHILDREN. Children are hypnotized by it because every single page is so interesting. It has ten volumes packed with mankind's finest literature."

The woman held up one of the volumes in her set of books. "Watch," she said.

She opened the book and held it before my eyes. I drooled and spit up on the first page. My mother blushed. "I don't think she's ready to read, yet," she said.

"Oh yes she is!" said Mrs. Mitchell. "Every child loves to read. You just need to give it stimulating fare. Whenever this little girl starts to whimper, put one of these books in her hand. If you have to leave her for a moment, let her have Volume One to play with. We have given the pages of that book a childproof coating to protect it from smudgy little fingers. These exciting doorways to the human mind will free you and enrich your child for years to come."

My mother had grown up in a house empty of books and her brother and sisters made a lot of racket all the time. She wanted me to keep quiet when she was talking to her friends or cleaning house and she didn't want me to scream when she was tired. Obviously, the way to do this was to let me play with books instead of dead end toys like rattles and jingling bells. "How much do these things cost?" she asked.

"Only one hundred dollars," said Mrs. Mitchell. "You can give me ten dollars today and pay the rest on our easy payment plan."

And that was the beginning of my love affair with the printed word. My mother put a book in my hand every time I cried, and whenever she left me alone. She read me nursery rhymes when she fed me and pointed to the pictures. I always ate everything on my plate although I was too absorbed in what I was hearing to taste a thing. "Eat that spinach," my mother would command.

"Read me one more page," I'd beg. "Just one more page. Please."

By the time Mama finished the page, the spinach was gone.

After Mrs. Mitchell sold us those ten books, my mother didn't bother to converse with me. Whenever we were alone, she read to me from MY BOOKHOUSE FOR CHILDREN. I was fascinated by the pictures and the remembered pleasure of snuggling under the covers while my mother recited those charming rhymes about Miss Muffet and that cute old woman who lived in a shoe. The books were colored a bright green and rich with pictures of their hidden treasures. I learned about a little boy from Norway who refused to part with the hat his mother knit him and I read about a tiny sparrow who sang its beautiful song despite this unbelievable handicap. The Uncle Remus stories made me laugh and the lyrical poetry evoked worlds I never heard about in radio soap operas like "Just Plain Bill" or "Our Gal Sunday. I became a fluent reader before I was two years old, but to this day, I cannot eat a meal without a book propped before me. This has precipitated several problems even as it unleashed my imagination.

When I entered kindergarten, the teacher took the entire class to the library and we received library cards. I was able to search for books by the same authors I had read in MY BOOKHOUSE and digested the complete Ivanhoe before I was eight and I still keep a volume of Emily Dickenson's poetry by my bedside.

From that day on, my mother's baby sitting problems were over. She dropped me off at the library with an afternoon snack and I wandered through the aisles finding gems of literature and beautiful illustrations to keep me amused until she had done her grocery shopping or met my Aunt Hazel for lunch. When she honked the horn outside the library, I would run to the door and shout," One more page, Mama! Just one more page. . . please?"

I had exhausted the books in the branch library when I was ten and, my mother taught me how to take the streetcar down to the main branch. I was out of her hair for at least four hours that way and she could go to the beauty shop, do volunteer work and play canasta at will.

My mother had very little interest in the written word and she never realized the printed pacifiers she had given me when I was a cranky little baby, would become my greatest treasure. I love the very smell of a new book and my home is filled with shelves of them from floor to ceiling. The only problem this addiction causes is when I am invited out for dinner. When everyone else puts their napkins in their laps, I prop up my book and dig in. "Aren't you afraid you'll miss some interesting conversation?" one hostess asked me and my eyes glazed over.

"Just one more page," I begged. " One more wonderful page."

Trivial Medication

Trifles make up the happiness . . . of mortal life.
-Alexander Smith

When the year 2000 ends, L. M. Boyd, that master of trivial facts no one cares about will give up his syndicated newspaper column and devote himself to more important pursuits. For me, that will be a great loss. For although he does not know it, it was this very man who gave me back my life.

I spent most of 1970 in the hospital listening to doctors at The National Institutes of Health tell me that they had finally figured out the remedy for my inexplicable illness. I could not digest the food I ate and despite a gargantuan appetite, I was dying of malnutrition. I was never without pain, doubled over with stomach spasms and blinded with headaches. I traveled a roller coaster of hope and despair for more than twelve months until, at last, I ripped the plastic I.D. from my wrist and insisted an attendant wheel me into a taxi bound for the Washington D.C. airport and home.

I weighed less than 60 pounds. My legs were like toothpicks; my eyes hollow caverns and my skin was transparent. My parents, who had written me off months before, barely hid their dismay at seeing this wraith that had once been their daughter arrive in Toledo, ready to be deposited in her mobile home to expire. For the next several months I only left the house to buy groceries that wouldn't stay in me long enough to do any good and wondered why the doctors' prophecies didn't come true. I decided that maybe those erudite men didn't have all the answers. They certainly weren't doing a medical thing worth discussing to me. "What did the cave man do when he got sick?" I asked myself. "He didn't rush to Mercy Hospital and wait for an emergency doctor to put him in a shroud. No, indeed! He ate the best he could, and exercised outdoors in fresh air.

I tried to follow this primitive example, but it was so difficult. My tummy hurt, my head throbbed and the slightest breeze threatened to tip me over. I would go outside dressed in my snowmobile suit, get violently ill and return home. I would eat huge and beautiful dinners and they would go through me like water down an open drain. Still, I forced myself outdoors every morning no matter what the weather, wrote my stories, did my art and read the newspaper as I pushed food down my throat. I never spoke to anyone but a gas station attendant and a grocery clerk, and I wrote the same story with different characters and painted the same picture in different colors over and over again. The only new ideas I absorbed arrived via the Toledo Blade. And that was where I discovered L. M. Boyd.

His column at that time was called CHECKING UP and it was filled with just the kind of trivia you scan while you are waiting for something to happen somewhere else. At the bottom of the piece was a request for contributions from readers for $5.00 a fact. As I read that column filled with information I didn't care about, I thought to myself, "I can do better than that."

I managed to get to a drugstore to buy 3x5 cards and I launched my newest and what would prove to be my shortest, yet most valuable career. I pondered the keys of my typewriter (that's what we used in those days) or stood at my easel, and let my mind wander into its storage bin of things I knew that no one else did. The first nugget I sent in was one my cat Michael taught me: Cats despise bathing. I typed this gem on a card and sent it to Mr. Boyd in Weatherford, Texas. After a few days, I decided it was as silly to wait for my payment as it was to count minutes until those doctors found a magic pill to keep food inside me. Mr. Boyd had thousands of entries to plow through before he discovered my little diamond. I sat down at my desk, thought for a while and then I smiled. Here was a fact only a lot of Eskimos and I knew: The national bird of Alaska is . . . THE MOSQUITO.

Now, I was hooked. Trivia became my motivating force. I would get up in the morning and think, "Sleep doesn't know how to knit." Not bad.

As I dressed it occurred to me that one dripping faucet uses fifty gallons of water EVERY MONTH! That was really a good one.

I looked outside at the children boarding the school bus and data rolled through my mind like a magic carpet: There is no such thing as an early birth; only tardy marriages. Children who eat breakfast learn faster than children who don't. All boys fight. That was $15.00 practically in the bank and I hadn't even started breakfast.

I heated the frying pan and threw in a double-yolked egg. "I wonder . . .", I said and called the local poultry growers association.

I knew they'd have my answer. Only one egg in 1,047 is double yolked and those are fathered by macho Bantams! A hen won't accept just any rooster. She has to like him. The most eggs are laid between March and May. And my most valuable fact, one contrary to everything I ever learned about the male sex: A rooster with a frozen comb will not even consider making love!

Amazing!

I threw out the charred remains of the egg in the frying pan and as I toasted my bread I realized Scandinavians toast potatoes for breakfast. French toast doesn't have an accent. A bagel can do severe damage to teeth. That was three I'd better write down before I forgot.

I donned my snowmobile suit and came up with a new one at every step. Fleas enjoy people. Chihuahuas do not bark in Spanish. Hitler's mother loved him. Married men die sooner than bachelors because they want to.

The months went by, the walks got longer, and my meals didn't have time to leave my body. I was far too absorbed in trivia to notice pain. My first acceptance came when I informed Mr. Boyd and his readers that toilets flush counter clockwise below the equator. I was elated. I had made the big time!

I wandered through life, my head in an encyclopedia, my fingers at the typewriter. Sour cream sours. Ninety-seven percent of the population cannot think. Rocking horses don't eat sugar. A latke is not a weapon. God won't lock your car. Labrador Retrievers cry real tears. Californians don't kill roaches; they smoke them.

And then my coup de grace: Napoleon wore cashmere underwear! I got $10.00, a certificate of merit and a thank you note from Mr. Boyd for that one. By that time, my food was digesting, my stories were selling and my paintings were hanging on walls other than my own. I was Lynn Ruth once more. It was my unexpected miracle and it all began the day I got so absorbed in CHECKING UP, I didn't have time to check out.

The great secret of doctors,
known only to their wives. . .
is that most things
get better by themselves.
- Lewis Thomas

The Night the Dog Bit Prince Charming

I will always remember New Year's Eve in 1950 because that was the night our dog bit Prince Charming.

The dog's name was Junior, a wirehaired terrier with a snappy walk an independent attitude. My mother adored him. Unfortunately for my father, the dog hated every member of his own sex. When he sniffed man, he attacked. My father insisted the dog was inflamed with envy because of early castration. "If you would have let him have one chance at it," he told my mother as she iodined his latest wound. "He'd be fine. But no, you trimmed him when he was barely weaned."

My mother shook her head and applied an especially large glob of disinfectant to my father's bleeding shins. "You are wrong," she said. "I know all about men. Once they start that business, they can't get enough of it. I fixed him just in time."

"Ouch!" screamed my father. "THAT HURT."

"I know," said my mother.

I didn't mind Junior 's temper until I started going out on dates. Any member of the male sex who rang our doorbell was at severe risk. "That dog is spoiling my social life," I told my mother. "Last month alone, he sliced three shins, got the sleeve of a flannel jacket and turned Jeremy's slacks into confetti."

"Dogs are excellent judges of character," said my mother. "Junior probably saved you from some very poor choices."

"I wouldn't know," I said. "The only thing I've ever said to a young man who crosses our threshold is, 'Don't be alarmed. I have just dialed 911."

"You're exaggerating," said my mother.

When I was a senior in high school, my date for New Year's Eve was Jimmy Peterman. He wore round horn rimmed glasses and was so tall, he looked like an owl perched on a matured oak tree. I had a desperate crush on him and when he asked me to join him to welcome 1950, I was on my way to heaven. Then I remembered Junior's phobia. "Do you want me to meet you at the party?" I asked.

"Oh no," he said. "I'll pick you up about seven. We'll have dinner first."

"Do you like animals?" I asked.

"I love them," he said. "And they love me."

"I certainly hope you're right," I said.

Promptly at seven, New Year's Eve, our doorbell rang. I ran to answer the door and my mother galloped after the dog. "You look beautiful," said Jimmy.

Junior bared his teeth and growled. My mother tightened her grip on the raging animal and her smile showed definite signs of strain. "He hasn't had supper yet," she said. "Now off you go. Have a wonderful time. "

We obeyed. We dined on prime rib and danced to the music of Sammy Kaye under a canopy of crepe paper streamers and helium balloons. It was when the band played "There's No Tomorrow", that I realized my mother would be asleep when Jimmy brought me home. "Isn't this a marvelous song?" said Jimmy. "I just love the words. They are so sad they bring tears to my eyes."

I nodded. "Mine, too," I said.

It was five in the morning when we finally climbed the steps of our porch. I unlocked the front door and Junior charged. In seconds, Jimmy Peterman stood before me, his trousers severed at the knee. "Oh my God," I cried.

I watched horrified as the blood trickled down his bared calves and stained the very argyle socks I had knitted for him for Christmas. My Prince Charming was as good as gone before I'd even received my New Year's kiss. I looked up at him and my eyes filled with tears.

But Jimmy Peterman 's expression showed no trace of anger or pain. He smiled at the snarling dog and reached out to pet him. "CAREFUL!" I cried, but he ignored me.

"Good boy!" he exclaimed. "I've always wanted a pair of Bermuda shorts! There isn't a store in town that makes them long enough for me."

He pointed to his ragged trousers. "See?" he said. "They're perfect! All they need is a hem."

He opened up his arms to hug me and I stood on my toes to receive his kiss. "It's going to be a very happy year," he announced. "And a wonderful summer. Do you like the beach?"

I nodded.

"We can take Junior with us," said Jimmy. "Would you like that?"

"No," I said and I kissed him back.

By keeping men off, you keep them on.
- John Gay

The Sponge Cake Disaster

When I was a freshman in high school, my Young Judea Club sponsored a citywide sponge cake bake-a-thon to raise funds for the community Passover Seder that spring. Passover commemorates the Book of Exodus in the Bible when Moses led the Israelites to freedom from the tyranny of the Egyptians. The eight-day holiday is launched with lavish meals the first two nights called Seders where the whole family gathers to pig out.

Observant Jews do not eat leavened foods during Passover to honor the ancestors who were forced to cross the desert on such short notice that they didn't have time to bake bread for their journey. Through the years, Jewish mamas have devised delicious substitutes for yeast breads that include the familiar matzo, muffins, popovers and a variety of sponge cakes leavened with beaten egg whites. My mother was a master at baking these delicious desserts and it was said that her sponge cakes were so light that if she opened a window in the kitchen, they would fly away. I was smack in the middle of teen-age rebellion at the time and I was certain that if my mother's cakes would fly out the window, mine would definitely ascend to heaven.

Fueled by this hormonal spurt of self-confidence, I entered the Young Judea contest, confident that I would walk away with the first prize, a free trip to the annual Young Judea convention in New York City. As soon as I completed the entry form, I began my packing list for the Big Apple.

Recipes for Passover sponge cakes have minor variations but their success depends on the amount of air beaten into the egg whites used. My mother's recipe called for 14 eggs separated, sugar and orange rind combined into the yolks and enough air to launch the Goodyear Blimp incorporated into the whites.

The morning of the day I was to enter the contest, I assembled the eggs and set out my utensils. I decided to frost my cake with whipped cream and use maraschino cherries to spell out JERUSULAM OF GOLD, the new hit single that had just come out of Israel that year. I would then fashion the musical notes of the song out of colored sugar candy and line them up along the sides of the cake.

By ten in the morning, I had beaten the egg yolks to the proper texture and added the orange rind and sugar. I put the fourteen egg whites in an immense bowl, attached them to my mother's Sunbeam Mixmaster and turned on the motor. I sat down with my novel and let electric power do the job. The book was excellent and it absorbed me completely for the next hour or so. When I looked at my gyrating bowl of egg whites, they were over the top and a very strange beige color. I finished the chapter I was reading, folded the yolk mixture into the whites and poured the whole thing into an angel food baking pan. There was so much batter that I had to haul out several loaf tins and a few casseroles to hold it all.

One hour later, I removed the cakes from the oven. They were golden brown and I was very proud. I turned the larger cake over to cool and began to address the other cakes when there was a loud whoosh and a deafening thud. I turned to see my cake tumble out of the pan.

I had only two hours before the contest entry deadline and I had already written for tickets to my favorite musicals. I scooped the remains of the cake into a large pan and layered it with whipped cream and several bottles of Manichevitz wine because its texture was disturbingly similar to glass marbles. The finished production was a spectacular collage of color, but when I tried to lift the platter it was so heavy, I almost dropped it. "It must be all that cream and wine," I thought. "No matter. Once the judges sample this, they'll be too drunk to even notice the other entries."

I wheeled the cake into the next room on a serving cart. "Can you help me lift this into the car?" I asked my mother. "I need to get it to the Community Center in about fifteen minutes."

My mother looked at the cake. It was bright with fruit and topping and resembled a cover picture for a recipe book. "It is really lovely, Lynn Ruth," she said. "And a very unusual shape for a sponge cake. Why do you need help putting it in the car?"

I flushed. "You try lifting it," I said.

My mother approached the serving cart and tried to move the cake platter.

She frowned and then braced her knee against the cart and tried again. "One of the criteria for a good sponge cake is its lightness," she observed. "I think you're in for a big disappointment."

"You never think I can do anything," I snapped. "Just because my cake is different from the ones you bake doesn't make it bad."

My mother looked at the product of my morning's work and nodded. "Right," she said.

Somehow, the two of us managed to haul my cake to the community center. I put it on the table with the other entries and smiled at the woman taking the entrance fees. "When will you notify the winners?" I asked.

I turned to see the legs on the table begin to buckle. “I better move this over to the book shelf,” I said.

That Friday night, the rabbi finished his sermon and then cleared his throat. “We had some very interesting entrants in the sponge cake contest, he said. “First prize goes to Gloria Rosenblatt who invented a wine and nut dessert with a peach filling. Good Baking, Gloria!”

My eyes filled with tears and my mother put her arm around my shoulder. “Listen!” she said.

“And honorable mention goes to Lynn Ruth Miller,” continued the rabbi. “Who created the very first doorstop that is kosher for Passover!”

The tragedy of life is not that man loses,
but that he almost wins.
- Heywood Broun

Singing in a Modern World

Extraordinary how potent cheap music is.
- Noel Coward

I love to sing. My mother swears my first sounds were melodies and my first words song requests. "Sing about 'Mary's lamb," I asked my mother when I was still in diapers.

"Let's sing together, darling," said Mama. "Mary had a little . . . '"

"Lamb!" I sang

My mother dropped her dust rag and wrapped her arms around me. "Wonderful! I want you to sing that song for Daddy when he gets home!"

That night, as soon as my father walked in the door, I welcomed him with a recital. "Why is she screaming?" he asked my mother.

"Are you deaf?" said Mama. "She's singing."

My first memory of school was the day I got a part in the class song fest. "I'm going to sing a solo at school," I told my mother. "I'm a teapot."

I cleared my throat and stood very tall. "I'm a little teapot, short and stout," I sang.

"Let's sing the song together, Lynnie," said my mother.

We were on the second chorus when my aunt walked in the door. She paused and then knelt beside me. "What's wrong, Lynn Ruth?" she asked. "Did you fall and hurt yourself?"

It was in the seventh grade that I got my first hint that I was not going to be a world class opera star. The teacher decided to teach us "Welcome, Sweet Springtime" for the annual May Festival.

"Welcome, sweet springtime, we greet the in sooong . . . " she sang.

As she walked down the aisle, she listened to our voices and smiled until she came to me. "You just mouth the words, dear," she whispered. "You're drowning out the others."

I turned my face away so she couldn't read the heartbreak in my eyes. "Sorry," I said.

Eventually, my mother tried to channel my musical interest into something more harmonically realistic. "How would you like to learn to play the accordion?" she asked. "You could sing and play at the same time."

After my first lesson, I gave my father a private performance when he came home from the office. I had to sing very loud to be heard above the huge, resonant sounds bellowing from the accordion but I was up to the challenge. I gave it my whole heart and soul, bending and swaying to the music. The combined sound of the instrument in my arms and my very healthy vocal chords actually splinted the furniture. My father 's smile froze on his face and his eyes glassed over. "Aren't you proud of her, honey?" said my mother. "Just imagine! She's only had one lesson!"

My father stared ahead, rigid as the wax effigies in Madame Troussant's Museum. "What's the matter, dear?" asked my mother. "Can't you hear me?"

Just then, three firemen rang our doorbell. One man held a rope ladder and another a very wicked looking axe. "What on earth is wrong?" my mother asked the three men. "We don't have a fire here."

"We know that, ma'am," said the one with the chemical spray can in his hand. "But one of your neighbors reported a stray animal caught under your house. We came over to see if we could help."

In college, I decided to become a kindergarten teacher so I could sing all through the day. When I entered my first classroom, I blew high C on my pitch pipe and began caroling in my deep mezzo voice, "Good morning to you!" I pulled up the window shades and sang "Let the merry sunshine in!" I chanted, "One little, two little, three little Indians . . . " When I taught numbers and when the children dressed for recess, I gave them my own syncopated arrangement of "Button up your overcoat."

Then one day, little Andrea tugged at my dress while I was doing a Latin version of "Where , oh where has my little dog gone . . . " and she said, "Mith Miller, why do all the thongs you thing have the thame tune?"

I paused mid-note and smiled. "No, sweetheart," I said. "Listen again."

"She's right," said Kenny. "All the songs you teach us are on the very same note."

In that awful moment, the musical failures of my past reeled before me and I knew that from the mouths of babes do indeed come truth. I am tone deaf. From that time on, I suppressed the melodies that bubbled inside me. My song was dead.

About a month ago, I turned my dial to KDFC and heard the announcer say, "Today, we are going to hear the latest lieder from that contemporary German composer, Wolfgang Vasserschnitz, who has taken the classical music world by storm. Soprano Natasha Passwater will be joined by tenor Jim Trickey and flutist Ralph Puckett. They will perform 'Snowflakes on the Amazon' an amazing modality that recreates the gentle falling of snowflakes in the mid day sun."

My radio actually shook with the shrieking, rumbles and violent trills of that duet. The flutist bleated A above high C while the tenor seemed to be praying for instant death. The soprano cried out her notes with such vigor that two glasses shattered on my kitchen shelf. At first, I thought the singer was having an appendicitis attack while she was passing a kidney stone. Then, I realized she was singing. "My goodness!" I told my darling radio. "I recognize that tune!"

I ran to my window and threw open the sash. I opened my mouth and released melodies that had been locked inside me for forty years. Oh, the joy of it! Oh the delight! There's a whole new world out there and everyone in it is singing my song!

Music is essentially powerless
to express anything at all.
- Igor Stravinsky

The Picnic That Went to the Dogs

When I was twelve, my cousin and I held a gala picnic for our family pets in honor of Independence Day. At that time, our dog was a wirehaired terrier named Junior who attacked all men. He hated moving feet of any sex and had a negative personality. My mother insisted that the dog was a finicky eater and broiled him ground round patties and beef heart, which made the animal remarkably bilious.

My cousin Jessica owned a canary named Tweety, a hamster she called Lizzie, two Siamese fighting fish named Bill and Coo and a pedigreed boxer christened Dell of the Everglades. This dog was a unique combination of exuberance and muscle, so full of joie de vivre that anyone who dared to walk him experienced the unique sensation of flying without benefit of propeller.

My Aunt Hazel had a very tiny cocker spaniel they called Sparky who loved to roll over and play dead. He did this at inappropriate times such as in front of my aunt's car when she pulled into the driveway or just after a heavy meal.

This was the summer of '44 when everything that tasted good was rationed and no one had enough gasoline to drive to a park. "What are we going to do for the 4th of July?" asked Jessica. "Our mothers are cooking for the USO. They said that if we wanted to have a picnic we'd have to make it ourselves."

"Why don't we give our pets a party?" I said. "I think they should know how much we love them."

Jessica's face brightened. "That's a great idea, Lynnie!" she said. "Dell just loves celebrations and the canary has been molting all week. He is very depressed. But I don't think I could stand to eat dog food. It has a terrible odor."

"My mother never feeds Junior dog food," I said. "She broils him expensive hamburgers and all we need to do is add a few onions to make them taste good."

"Sparky can't eat meat," said Jessica. "He has a delicate digestive system and can only have rice."

"We'll mix the ground meat with rice. He'll probably love it that way." I said.

" Why don't we frost dog biscuits red, white and blue for dessert?" said Jessica. "Dell has such a sweet tooth that he jumps on the dining room table when my mother serves chocolate cake."

"I'll ask Mother to save sugar coupons and buy some food coloring," I said. "Should we have ice cream, too? It will be good for Junior. He has shallow bones."

" Can I bring the hamster, the bird and the goldfish?" asked Jessica.

"Why not?" I said. "Mary Kaplan has a cute little kitty named Elizabeth that we can invite and Aunt Hazel said she couldn't leave her parrot at home because he is on anti-depressants."

On the morning of our Big Event, Jessica arrived with a basket of frosted dog biscuits, peanut butter pralines for the hamster and a bowl of minnows for the goldfish. "What about Tweety and Aunt Hazel's parrot Cyril?" I asked. "We don't have any bird seed."

"Tweety is molting again, so he's on a liquid diet," said Jessica. "I brought his bottle of Seagrams. We can share it with everyone."

"Okay," I said. "Lets pour a little in the dog bowls as an appetizer."

The dogs lapped up that whisky like it was honey and pretty soon all of them were whirling around the yard as if someone had wound them up with a key. The birds were screaming from their cages and Lizzie was squeaking like an ungreased wheel. The cat had lunged to the top of the garage and sounded like an opened fire hydrant.

"I think it's time to eat," I said to Jessica.

Jessie and I set out big platters of hamburgers, onions, frosted dog biscuits and peanut butter candy on the picnic table. "I'll bring out the plates," I said but Jessica shook her head.

"Too late," she said.

I looked at the ravaged table. It was turned on its side and Dell was gazing at it while he chewed up the last of the forks. "How did Lizzie get in that tree?" I asked.

Jessica frowned. "She jumped. I think Dell thought she was dessert."

"Where's Tweety?" I asked.

"He's huddled in a corner in his cage. I've never seen him shake like that," said Jessica. " I'm really hungry. Where did you put our hamburgers?"

"On the platter," I said.

Jessica's eyes filled with tears. "Oh," she said.

"I think I saw a bag of Ken L Ration in the pantry," I said. "My mother keeps it for emergencies."

"I wonder how it tastes with mustard?" said Jessica.

I opened up four cans of Ken-L-Ration and put the contents under the broiler. It didn't smell bad exactly, but it didn't smell good either. I put the dog food into hamburger buns and arranged them on the platter. Just then my mother and my aunt pulled into the driveway. "I am ravenous!" said my mother. "Those boys ate like it was their last meal!"

"It might very well be," said my aunt. "Oh look! Lynnie made hamburgers!"

She beamed at me.

Jessica and I watched horrified while our hungry mothers gobbled up dog food sandwiches and the dogs lapped up the ice cream I had brought out for dessert. "Should we tell them?" said Jessica.

"Let's sneak over to Mrs. Zarneckie's," I said. There must be one hundred drunken relatives in their back yard. They'll never notice us."

As we tiptoed out the back door, I heard my mother exclaim, "These are really delicious! What did Lynnie do to them?"

"I think she used some garlic," said my aunt. "Would you like another?"

Melvin?

February fourteenth had always been a bleak day of empty mailboxes and broken dreams for me until I came West. My very first Valentine's Day there, I found a tremendous bouquet of flowers waiting for me at my front door. I had been waiting for a moment such as this for almost fifty years. I galloped up the steps and tore at the green wrapping paper to find the card that would tell me that someone I had met in my new hometown actually loved me. I opened the little envelope and read, "Happy Valentine's day from Melvin."

I paused. I couldn't think of one eligible man in my generation with that name. In fact, I was hard put to remember any Melvin until I recalled the lovely young man who was the house manager for Stanford's Lively Arts. I had done a bit of ushering for him and he probably sent a bouquet to all the little old ladies who helped him. I sat down immediately and wrote him an effusive thank you note.

Two days later, there was a knock at my door. I opened it and Melvin stood on my front porch, his face red as a valentine heart and a dozen roses in his hand. "I didn't send you flowers for Valentines' Day, Miss Miller," he said. "But I should have. You have been a wonderful help to me this year."

I thanked him. I hugged him. I plied him with cake and coffee and swore I would usher for him until that university crumbled to the ground. I kissed him good by and leaned against my front door and searched my memory in vain.

I didn't know another Melvin.

Suddenly I remembered that cute carry out boy at Key Market. We always made jokes together and I flirted with him shamelessly. I hurried to the store and when darling little Melvin started to bag my groceries, I wrapped him in my arms and kissed him. "Aren't you PRECIOUS!" I exclaimed. "That bouquet of flowers was the nicest Valentine I have ever received!" and I was telling the absolute truth.

The trouble was I was telling the truth to the wrong man or should I say boy? Melvin was twelve years old.

While I was paying for my groceries, Melvin disappeared for a moment. He returned with an immense bouquet of daisies in his hand and a helium balloon that said BE MINE. He thrust both objects in my arms and picked up my sacks of food. "I meant to get these to you in time," he lied. "But I wasn't paid until this morning."

"I see," I said.

I returned home and I wept. How could life could be so cruel? Somewhere in this world there was a man named Melvin who loved me enough to send me flowers and I didn't have the faintest notion who he was. I called the florist who delivered my valentine and asked who had ordered the mystery flowers. He explained that he was not allowed to divulge that information. "What's your first name?" I asked.

"Sebastian," he said. "Sebastian O'Malley. Why do you ask?"

I was too choked up to answer. I stared at my three bouquets and then I stopped crying. I sat back and admired them. I inhaled their perfume and swore I would name my next dog Melvin. I looked up in the general direction of heaven and I said. "Oh thank you, Melvins of the world! I will cherish the memory of my very first Valentine Triple Header as long as I live!"

And I do.

Love ceases to be a pleasure when it ceases to be a secret.
- Aphra Behn

How Life Begins

Unto the pure, all things are pure.
-The Bible

When I was eleven years old, my mother gave me a picture book called HOW LIFE BEGINS. It began with a photograph of a bee hovering over a very provocative flower and ended with a mother feeding her baby, but I never really understood what it was trying to get across until my sixth grade class put on an Easter bunny race at Ottawa Hill.

My current romantic interest was a boy named Billy Kalb, but I was not his. His fascination was with all animals not human. He was a shy boy, whose home teemed with exotic birds, lizards, hamsters and even a flea circus that he observed on a daily basis. I managed to talk my parents into letting me enter the Easter contest because that would give me lots of opportunity to ask his advice and get him to notice me.

My bunny was a tiny white female with a fluffy tail and a sweet disposition. I named her Gloria. Billy's was a large, aggressive buck named Matthew. "He has a nasty little temper, doesn't he?" I said to Billy after Matthew took a hunk out of my finger.

Billy smiled. "I know he does," he said. "That's why I chose him. I want to win the race."

I nodded. "I want to win, too," I said, but I didn't add that it wasn't the contest I wanted to win. It was Billy Kalb's heart. "Gloria is very fast, and your rabbit has an obvious weight problem."

Billy sneered. "He is muscular," he said. "I work him out every day. Your rabbit is soft as a powder puff. She doesn't have a chance."

"We may surprise you," I said.

The morning of the race, all the sixth graders gathered at the top of Ottawa Hill. Every contestant had his rabbit at the starting line and held a carrot to dangle in front of its nose. The idea was that the rabbit would follow the carrot down the hill and the first rabbit to cross the finishing line would win.

Gloria and I had been practicing this routine for about a month but for some reason, Gloria was not particularly fond of carrots. She preferred something sweeter, like chocolate cake. I decided that the best way to keep her moving down the hill was to dip the carrot in honey. I did not really want her to beat Matthew, but I wanted her to come in second. That way I would accomplish a double purpose. Billy would admire me, but he would still feel just superior enough to keep his ego intact.

I managed to get the place next to Billy and Matthew at the starting line. I stroked Gloria and gave her coat another brush. I smiled at Billy. "Matthew looks fit," I observed. "But I really think you should have put him on a diet. His tummy actually drags on the ground."

"This rabbit is so fast he will get down to the bottom of this hill before yours manages to get out of her cage," said Billy. "Why did you put that pink ribbon around her neck, and that fancy barrette between her ears? "

I blushed. "Well, I thought she'd feel better if I dressed her up a little. After all, this is her first public appearance."

Our sixth grade teacher clapped her hands to get our attention and smiled. "When I ring the bell, let your rabbits out of their cages," she said. "The winner will receive a basket of chocolate Easter eggs and a year's supply of rabbit food. May the best bunny win!"

At the sound of the gong, Matthew shot out of his cage. Gloria stood at the open door and gazed at the scenery. "Come on, Gloria," I urged and I waved a honey-dipped carrot in front of her. "Show everyone how fast you can run."

Gloria sniffed the spring air and wiggled her ears. Her gaze moved toward Matthew and she began to run over to him. Matthew ran a few yards after the carrot Billy dangled in front of him and then stopped. He turned around and hopped over to Gloria. Within moments, he had jumped on top of her and seemed to be glued to her in a most alarming way. I was fascinated. "Billy!" I said. "What on earth are they doing?"

Billy blushed purple. "They are making love!" he exclaimed. "Your rabbit must be in heat!"

I shook my head. "She didn't feel particularly warm to me," I said. "I really think Matthew is very lazy to expect my little bunny to give him a ride down this hill."

"You don't know anything!" said Billy. "And both of us have lost the race."

I took his hands in mine. "Oh don't worry about it," I said. "Everyone knows what a good animal trainer you are and besides the prize wasn't worth that much. I got a beautiful basket of eggs and candy from my Aunt Hazel and I'll share it with you."

Billy smiled. "That's really nice of you," he said. "I'll help you get Gloria home as soon as they're done."

"Done with what?" I asked.

That day I learned that our need for love is far greater than our need for food and when it comes to successful romance, sharing is a better strategy than competition. But it wasn't until a month later when Gloria presented me with her litter that I finally realized how life begins.

Time ripens all things.
- Cervantes

The Purim Pageant

The Jewish holiday Purim celebrates the triumph of the beautiful Queen Esther of Persia who risked her life to save the Jewish people. When her husband's minister, Haman, was insulted by her Uncle Mordecai, Haman retaliated by convincing King Ahasuerus that all Jews were lawbreakers and should be destroyed. Esther had not discussed her religious beliefs with her husband and when she heard this news, she knew she was in deep trouble. Instead of confronting her husband and begging him to spare her people, she invited both him and Haman to a sumptuous banquet so elaborate it took two days to consume. The king obviously loved her cooking because by the time they got to dessert he told her that she had won his heart and anything else she wanted. "You don't owe me a thing, darling," said the clever Queen Esther. "It's always a pleasure to cook for good eaters. But if you want more dinners like this, you will have reverse your order to slaughter the Jews because I am Jewish."

King Ahasuerus was no one's fool. He knew that charming, beautiful wives who were artists in the kitchen were definitely not a dime a dozen and he wasn't going to lose the one he had. He executed Haman, saved the Jews and made Uncle Mordecai the big shot in the community.

A decision like that deserves a celebration, and the Jewish people honor Esther's victory with lavish feasts, hot music and masquerades. They give food and gifts to the poor, and serve three-cornered cookies named after the villain Haman, filled with laxative fruits like prunes and raisins.

I have always loved the panache and carnival atmosphere of the holiday but I never understood how clever and strong Esther was until the year my fifth grade Sunday School class reconstructed the Bible story in a pageant we presented to the entire congregation.

The obvious choice to be Queen Esther was Dolores Shapiro, the most beautiful girl in our class. Freddie Okun was King Ahasuerus because he was so adorable, no one could resist him. Larry Zaft got to be Mordecai because he was painfully shy and the teacher thought it would be good for his ego to play the nice guy. Buddy Glasier was chosen to be Haman because he was the tallest boy in our class and leered ominously if no one made him laugh. I adored him but he never even noticed me because he was in love with Dolores Shapiro.

We started rehearsing our play the beginning of February but right after Valentine's Day, Dolores caught the mumps. That was when I got my big chance. The teacher decided that I could be the courageous queen because no one else could memorize all the lines fast enough.

The parents were in charge of costuming their children. My mother wanted me to be presentable when I appeared on stage but that would not be an easy task. At that time in my life, there was very little that was regal about me. I wore braces on my teeth and outsized orthopedic oxfords because my arches had collapsed in ballet class. I was painfully thin and my mother tried to build me up by feeding me high calorie foods that gave me terrible gas and an uncertain complexion. My hair was very fine, and the only way my mother could keep it under control was to braid it so tightly that my eyes developed an oriental slant.

She couldn't find a crown that would stay on my head and finally resorted to taping a rubber band on one she found in a costume shop that was obviously made to fit Humpty Dumpty. The only gown that would cover my bloated middle was one of her old maternity dresses. "Queens are supposed to wear velvet robes," I told my mother. "Not cotton prints with expandable waists."

"You will look very regal, Lynnie Ruth," she assured me. "As long as you don't smile. Those braces tend to catch the light."

The night of the performance, I stood center stage with my crown resting precariously on my eyebrows and tried not to trip on the sagging hem of my dress. I wore an apron over it and carried a cooking spoon to indicate that I had spent hours over a hot stove creating the dinner that would turn the tide for my people. Freddie wiped his mouth on one of his mother's damask napkins and decided to improvise his lines. "What a marvelous dinner, honey!" he declared. "Where did you get all those recipes?"

I didn't remember that cue when we rehearsed the play and I had to think very fast. "I always use the Hadassah cookbook," I told him. "And I'm glad you like dinner because this one will have to be your last."

Freddie was really into the mood of the piece by this time and he shook his head dramatically. "Oh no!" he exclaimed. "I was counting on apple knishes for next Friday night."

"Well," I said. "You will have to order some from Brauers because next Thursday, a bunch of thugs are going to do me in."

Freddie paused and tried to remember what to say next. There was some rustling of programs and then Larry Zaft, his face beet red, whispered something in Freddie's ear. "My God!" said Freddie. "Are you Jewish? No wonder you're such a good cook! This is terrible news. Who is going to do such a thing to you?"

I paused and took a deep breath. This was the moment that would make me famous and save the day for all the Jews. I pushed my crown out of my eyes and I turned to face Haman. The audience was silent and I squared my shoulders. Buddy Glasier leered at me in his very best manner and I faltered. He was really very handsome and I adored him. I just couldn't say the words that would send him to the gallows and make the audience boo him off the stage.

I swiveled around and pointed my finger at Larry Zaft. "He is the villain!" I hissed.

"I am not!" cried Larry and his eyes filled with tears. "I'm your uncle!"

By this time, Buddy had recovered from his shock at being saved. "You're not even Jewish, you fraud," he said and he leered in his most ferocious manner. "You have been hatching a secret plot to destroy all the Jews around here and I'm going to help Esther save them."

The shock was too much for Larry and he wet his pants. The teacher sidestepped the puddle that was spreading into the footlights and smiled at the astonished congregation. "Wonderful improvisation, boys and girls!" she exclaimed. "And now it's time for our parade. Let's have everyone join hands and dance around the auditorium while our hospitality mothers put out the hamantaschen."

The audience applauded and Buddy Glasier took my hand for the curtain call. "You were really clever," he said. "That ending was a wonderful surprise."

I blushed. "Why thank you!" I said, "But it was your quick thinking that stole the show."

"Happy Purim, Queen Esther," he said.

And indeed it was. . . the happiest Purim I ever had.

The mind of a woman is capable of anything
-Heard at a hen party

Saving the Downtrodden

"No one can make you feel inferior without your consent."
-Eleanor Roosevelt

When I was five, I decided I wanted to be like President Roosevelt's wife, Eleanor when I grew up. Her entire life was dedicated to others and it was her encouragement that gave Franklin the will to pursue his destiny despite his polio. "We are privileged to have someone like Eleanor Roosevelt in the White House," my mother told me. "She is always ready to protect the downtrodden."

"Are we downtrodden?" I asked my mother.

"Not yet," she said. "But if we were, Eleanor Roosevelt would come to our aid."

"Is Dale Brodsky downtrodden?" I asked and my mother nodded.

"You could call him that," she said.

Dale Brodsky's father was the janitor of our building and he lived in the basement with his parents and his four little sisters. I knew they were very poor because my mother sent me downstairs with our leftover food almost every night and whenever we cleaned out our closets she gave everything I had outgrown to Dale's little sisters.

Every afternoon, Dale cut school to watch the trains come into the station. "I just love trains," I told Dale. "Do you think you could take me to the station sometime?"

"Sure," said Dale. "How about this Saturday?"

"I'll have to ask my mother," I said. "She's the one who makes all the decisions in our house."

"My father is in charge of our house," said Dale. "He says women are worthless."

"They are NOT," I said. "Just who do you think is the most important person in this country?"

"The president!" said Dale. "He's in charge of everything."

"Wrong!" I said. "Eleanor Roosevelt is the one who runs the White House and she helps downtrodden people like you."

"Eleanor Roosevelt ain't done a thing for me," said Dale. "My father said its them fools in Washington who step all over the little guy and won't let him earn a decent wage. That's why we're so poor."

"My mother says you are only poor if you think you are. She told me just yesterday that the best things in life are free," I retorted.

Dale put his hand on his hips. "Yeah?" he said. "Name one."

I was on solid ground here. I knew loads of free things that were great. "A rainbow!" I said triumphantly.

"You can't wear a rainbow when it's pouring outside," said Dale.

"Well I know that, " I said. "But who would want to wear a rainbow anyway? You're supposed to just look at it."

"Listen, said Dale. "If you follow me, I'll give you something to look at that really is the best and it doesn't cost a cent."

By this time the sun was very low in the sky there was a breeze sweeping through the trees. "Let me go in the house to put on a sweater," I said.

"You're a sissy!" said Dale.

"No, I'm not," I said. "I'm just cold."

Dale put his arm around me. "I'll keep you warm," he said.

I followed him behind the garage and looked around. All I saw was a broken wheelbarrow and Dale's bicycle with the pedal missing. "I don't see anything that wonderful back here," I said.

Dale nodded. "But you will," he said and took down his trousers. I looked at him and I still didn't see anything very amazing. "Now you take off your pants and we can really have fun!"

I shook my head. "Eleanor Roosevelt would never do a thing like that," I said. "Even for the downtrodden!"

I turned and ran into the house. My mother looked up from the stove as I ran in the door, the tears running down my face. "There you are!" she exclaimed. "I was just going outside to find you. What were you doing?"

"I was trying to be kind to the needy," I said. "But it didn't work."

My mother waved her spatula at me and looked very righteous. "Sometimes, people don't value the good things you do for them, Lynnie Ruth," she said. "But that mustn't stop you. It is our obligation to humanity to help others no matter how little they appreciate our efforts."

"Dale told me there was something wonderful inside his jeans but all I saw was his dirty underwear," I informed my mother. "Would Eleanor Roosevelt have seen something else?"

My mother paused and then she nodded. "Lynn Ruth," she said. "A lot of men are going to tell you that, but they are wrong. Life gives us many better opportunities for happiness than anything we can get when we take off our clothes."

"I don't understand . . ." I said and my mother kissed me.

"I know you don't, honey. But Eleanor Roosevelt does."

Do what you feel in your heart to be right -
for you'll be criticized anyway.
- Eleanor Roosevelt

Jessica

Friday! I rub the sleep from my eyes and stretch to meet the morning sun. Tonight, I will be a mother once again. Tonight, I will begin my week-end with Jody and Ben.

The time with my babies is so close, I fondle it like a soft ball of fur. My angels! I caress their picture on my dresser. Jody clutches her teddy and looks up at her daddy with huge green eyes. Ben is still too small to have any expression but baby contentment. He is barely two in the picture; Jody, four. It was taken over a year ago when Mark and I were still working to keep our marriage together. We both tried to patch our tattered relationship for the children's sake; and finally we realized it was no use. And so we separated . . . that, too, for the children's sake. I recall our terrible fights as I pull my hairbrush through my hair . . . hard. My scalp screams just as Mark did that cheerless, winter night we gave up mending the worn out fabric of our life together.

"What held you up this time?" he demanded. "Look at Jody, still in her filthy pinafore! Ben's hands are black with dirt. Why can't you wash these children before they come to the table?"

"I didn't get out of the dress shop until late. Then I had to stop at the store to buy food. By the time I picked up the children at the day care center, it was six o'clock. The minute the three of us opened the door, you complained that your dinner wasn't on the table. Just when was I supposed to find time to get them washed and bandbox fresh to dine with their daddy? Just when?"

"My mother always found time for me, even when she worked to help Dad out. You only have an afternoon job. Why can't you manage to make enough room for us in your life?"

He took Ben in his arms and held Jody's hand. They stood together across the table from me, a wall of stubborn resistance. "Everyone thinks they deserve more room in someone else's life," I said. "I wanted more of my mother, too, but she never had time for me, either."

I tear at the lace on my bathrobe now, trying to erase the anger I feel still . . . at my mother. . . at Mark. How could he be so unjust? I sacrificed my own dreams for his. I quit school to marry him before he started business school. After he graduated, we melted into middle class America. He was a young executive on his way up the corporate ladder and I was a very pregnant Mrs. Suburbia. At first, all I could think of was feeding times and diaper changing. But once the toilet training days were over, I wanted some special treats for my babies. I began to work at an exclusive clothing store downtown. After I started my job, we had enough money for fancy clothes for Jody and darling "little man" suits for Ben. I indulged my darlings with foolish toys and delightful expeditions, and I loved it.

Be fair, Jessica. You indulged yourself, too. You used your discount at Juliette's to splurge on fine designer clothes you couldn't resist.

I must stop this day dreaming and decide what to wear. I want to look smart for my customers today, and bright for my darlings, tonight. A vivid print blouse and a soft cream suit. Yes. With beige shoes and bag. I ponder my collection of earrings and pins. I hold my blue beads in my hand and twist them tight as I remember Mark's hateful voice once again. "You're a fool, Jessica. Kids don't need fancy clothes. They need love they can count on. You can't buy that and wrap it up with a ribbon. You have to give children yourself . . . and that takes time."

Time. I never have enough time to do anything, even now. "You're always going somewhere," Mark complained. "You're off to your job or running to school at night to get your degree. We never see you except for a minute or two at dinner. You're lucky the kids even recognize you."

The fury I feel now is as fresh as I felt then. The beads in my hand break apart just as I did when Mark attacked me. "You listen here," I snapped. "When I waited table at Humphry's to help pay for your MBA, I was never home. You didn't mind that. Now, it's my turn. Why are you complaining when I'm trying to earn my own tuition? I want my college degree, too, and I'm willing to work for it just like I worked for yours."

I sat down at the table. "Jody. Stop picking at your food."

"Don't force her to eat those greasy packaged dinners you buy at the Seven Eleven. I never tasted a TV dinner until I married you. Now, I never taste anything else."

I opened my mouth to answer when I heard the crash of broken glass. I felt the chill of milk filling my shoes and spattering my legs even before I saw it pouring from Ben's high chair. "Oh, Ben! Why can't you watch what you're doing? Now, I've got to clean you up and mop the floor, too. I'll be late for class again!"

I look now at my bottles of makeup and perfume. I have dropped the Arpege in the sink. I choke on its rich sweetness and choke on the words I screamed that terrible night. My voice was so shrill that Jody started to cry. Her screams mingled with Ben's insulted sobs. "Why do you scold everybody, Mama?" Jody said. "Are we all being bad?"

Instant remorse cooled my fury. "I'm sorry, baby," I said. "I didn't realize how horrid I sound."

Mark picked up our daughter and wiped away her tears. "Finish your salad, Jody. I'll make you some scrambled eggs with tomatoes instead of that cardboard casserole your mother calls food. Okay?"

"But I like creamed chicken and bacon bits!" Jody cried, clutching her plate.

"You see what you've done? You've taught them to eat greasy junk food that will destroy their teeth and beef up their cholesterol. What kind of a mother are you?

"Stop crying, Jody. And you, too, Ben. Daddy will get you some nice clean food while Mommy washes you up."

"Wash them up yourself. You can play Mama all you want," I shouted. "I'm leaving. I have to get to school."

"Good. Go to school. Study your retailing and let me get this place back together again. We're all done with you, Jessica. Finished. You needn't bother to come back."

I can still feel my heart thumping so hard my chest ached. I grabbed my books and ran to the car. My thoughts spun faster than the wheels of the speeding Toyota. He can't have my babies. He just can't. No judge in the world would make me give them up.

But no judge had to take Jody and Ben from me. I gave them to Mark myself. I look at their picture now and try to explain to their sweet faces frozen in their baby smiles. "I didn't want you to suffer because your daddy and I couldn't live together. I wanted you to eat fine food and do fun things, and those are the luxuries Mark can provide.

At first, I hoped your daddy would pay us enough child support so I could give you a comfortable life, myself. But he fought every penny I demanded because he wanted to keep you with him. My lawyer warned me that I'd have to chase after his money every month. "At first, his check will be a few days late and then, pretty soon, it won't be in your mailbox at all, Jessica. I've seen it happen time after time," he said.

"But he can't do that! It's against the law!"

"It takes time and money to fight for your rights in court, Jessica. And who will pay your grocery bills during his postponements and appeals?"

"I will," I said.

And I did try to pay our bills after Mark and I separated. Oh, how I tried! But my salary isn't enough to buy you nice things. Remember? Remember how little I saw you then? How empty our lives were? I rushed to work; I dashed to school; and I volleyed you back and forth between the day care center and the baby sitter. Life was a frugal nightmare.

Remember?

And so, I gave you up. It broke my heart then. And the sore place still won't heal.

Tears of regret stain the scarlet flowers on my blouse. I want to be your bright, sweet flower, just as you are mine. But I know I'm only fooling myself. My velvet dream of our weekend together is too smooth to be true. I don't like to think about what will really happen when I take you home with me. I don't like to recall the way Jody cries for her daddy or Ben won't eat what I cook. "I want to go home," says Ben.

"This is your home, too," I say and Jody laughs.

"This isn't our house, Mommy. There's no apple tree to climb and no tire to swing on."

"I want my fuzzy bear. I want him right now," whines Ben every time I put him in my car. Every single time.

I make my bed quickly and glance at the two roll-away cots that await my babies tonight. No room of their own, here. No feeling of warmth and comfort no matter how many treats I buy; no matter how much I try to wrap them in a soft cloud of love.

In the beginning, it wasn't this way. When I took them back to Mark, Jody clung to me and cried, "Don't leave, Mommy. Take me with you!"

And Ben: "Me, too, Mama. Me too."

But it's been a year now and I've become just a visitor to my babies. They see more of Abbey than they do me. And I hate it.

I don't have time to think of all that now. I must hurry or I'll be late for work. I straighten the apartment and put Jody's dolls around the little doll house I couldn't resist at Toys-R-Us. I set up a small table with Ben's hammer and nails and his wooden train. I leave at last and drive to the Seven Eleven to buy peanut butter. Oh, yes, and fruit rolls for Ben. Jody likes yogurt. What flavor was it? Mocha mint? No. Strawberry apple. That's it. I'll buy these Oreos, too. Maybe they'll like them better than the jelly doughnuts they ignored last time.

I rush to the dress shop and will the hours to move swiftly. "Yes, that green is perfect on you, Mrs. Drager. It goes with your eyes."

And it matches my Jody's eyes even more. Oh, hurry, HURRY, Mrs. Drager. Buy your green chiffon dress and let me wrap a few hours of this never-ending day in its box. But there are Mrs. Bordens and Miss Elwoods, twill coats and tweed suits yet to endure before this Friday ends. At last, I grab my bag and my blazer and shout good bye to Juliette.

I brace myself to fight the sandwiched traffic on the long commute to my old house. I fill my mind with all the things I will do with my darlings this weekend. I'll bake that frozen pizza I bought last week and open a can of spaghetti for dinner. We'll have ice cream and hot fudge while we watch that Disney movie on TV. Tomorrow, I'll take them to the zoo and buy them cotton candy. And Sunday? Wonderful, relaxing Sunday! We'll sleep late and I'll toast some waffles for brunch. We'll be a snugly family once again in my cold, barren rooms. Oh, please, dear God. Just once, don't make me an intruder throwing pebbles in my babies' lives. My heart cries to hear Jody singing as she plays, to see the laughter burst from Ben's liquid brown eyes.

Just once.

I exit the freeway and drive through peaceful suburban streets. I feel the quiet beauty of the manicured lawns and flower sprinkled hedges I left. I pull into the driveway that once was mine. Not a child is in sight.

How strange it feels to be ringing the bell of the home I created. I tap my foot. Where is Mark? Why doesn't he answer? At last, the door opens. It's Abbey. I can smell the bread baking, see a flour smudge on her blouse. She wipes her hands on her apron and nods. "Hello, Abbey. The children are all ready for you but Jody has a stomach ache. Mark is trying to talk her out of it, now."

Only my lips smile. I try to enter the house. "I'll talk to her. Sometimes, Mommies have a way of soothing sore tummies."

Abbey blocks my way. We both know this mommy creates the pain that Jody feels. "No. You better wait here," she says.

I hear Jody's wails of protest and know Abbey is right. "Where is Ben?"

This time, I push past her and hurry to the backyard. There he is, starchy clean in his little white shirt and red bow tie. He is swinging on the battered tire Mark and I salvaged from the junkyard in the days when we tried to be a couple. "Hi, honey!" I call. "Are you ready for our adventure?"

He pretends he doesn't hear me. I run to him and lift him off the swing. "Let me stay a little longer, Mommy." He begins to cry. "The air feels so good on me."

I lift him down and grasp his hand. "Did you bring me a present?" he says.

His short, stubby legs race to match my long strides. "I have lots of presents for you at my place," I say.

"But I don't want to leave yet! I'll miss 'The Adventures of Bertha Bear.' Can't we wait 'til it's over?"

We enter the house. Jody stands beside Mark clutching her Barbie doll. Her eyes are red and swollen. Her thumb is in her mouth. Mark smoothes her hair and Ben takes her hand. "I think she's ready, now, Jessica," Mark says. "But before you leave, I have some things we'd better settle. Next Wednesday, Jody is going to a birthday party. Would you mind changing your day?"

I stiffen. "Yes, I would mind very much."

I am very firm. I see my wonderful Wednesday melting away like ice cream on a hot day. My voice is cold, defensive. "My class meets on Tuesdays and Thursdays and Friday begins your weekend. Wednesday is my only day."

I pause. I keep my voice neutral, now. I must not betray the hope that begins to bubble inside me. "I'll give you Wednesday if you let me have them this weekend. How's that?"

"Don't you remember?" Mark is polite, but as determined as I. "Abbey and I are taking them to the beach. I told you that. The children have been talking about our trip for days. You wouldn't want to disappoint them, would you? Besides, this is our celebration. I'm explaining to them about Abbey and me."

"What about Abbey and you?"

"We're getting married next month. The children love her and so do I."

"I see."

I swallow the lump of defeat that chokes me. I take Jody's hand and lift Ben in my arms. "It's getting awfully late. We have to go."

"Where's my blankie?" asks Ben.

"I'll get it," says Abbey.

She hurries into the back bedroom. She returns with a tattered blue blanket and a panda bear. "I brought you Brucie to keep you company," she says. "He'll kiss you goodnight instead of me."

Ben reaches out to kiss her. "Goodnight, Abbey," he says.

"Kiss me, too," says Jody."

I put the children in the car. "I need to go back in the house," says Jody.

"Why?"

"I forgot to water my plant. It's thirsty."

"You can do that on Sunday."

I start the car. Ben stands up on the car seat. Jody jabs at the buttons on the radio. A cacophony of music drowns out the honk and roar of the expressway. My head throbs. I need to think but fury numbs my mind.

So. They're getting married. Abbey will cook my children's dinner and put them to bed each night. She'll be the good fairy when Jody loses her first tooth. She'll cuddle my Ben when he wakes in the middle of the night. Abbey. Not me.

I pull the car to a screaming halt in the parking lot. The three of us enter my apartment. "We're having pizza and spaghetti tonight before we watch television," I say. "Won't that be fun?"

"Where is my present?" asks Ben.

"Why can't we have tuna fish?" asks Jody.

Ben picks up a dish of jelly beans. It drops on the floor. Shards of glass mingle with a dancing rainbow of confection. "I want tuna fish, too," he whines.

"You sit down," I snap. "Play with your building blocks or something while I clean up this mess."

"I want Abbey," he screams.

The children's racket fades into the roar of my own frustration. My babies aren't mine anymore and I am determined to get them back. That woman is not going to be what I could have been if I hadn't made myself a martyr. I call my lawyer. He'll do something. I know he will.

But he isn't in. His secretary says he'll call me Monday.

My voice tightens. "This is an emergency. You have him call tonight."

I slam down the receiver and return to broken glass, scattered jelly beans and screaming children. The front door opens.

"Well, Jessica," says my mother. She stands very still, framed in the entrance, a chilling glacier in the heat of our chaos. "I stopped in to kiss my grandchildren."

She looks around and clicks her tongue. "This place is a garbage can."

She glances at the littered kitchen counter, at the children's playthings. "Haven't you fed them yet? It's almost seven."

"Just what do you think I'm trying to do?"

She moves into the cluttered living room. Disgust distorts her face. "I'll get the children washed up and you start dinner."

"I can handle it, Mother. Leave me alone."

"Ben," she says. "How did your hands and face get so sticky? Careful, don't mess my new blouse. Has your mother been giving you candy?"

She looks down at the rug littered with broken glass and jelly beans. "I see," she says.

"We had cookies in the car, Grandma. I want more cookies," Jody whines.

I stand at the kitchen cabinet. Where's that can of spaghetti? It must be hidden behind the Minute Rice. I bite my lip and begin taking out all the cans and boxes. I slam them down on the counter. "Mark and Abbey are getting married next month."

"Good for Mark! Abbey's magic with those kids. They adore her, and why not? They're the center of her world. She'd never trade them in for an apartment nearer work."

I swallow the furry that rises in my throat. Who is this woman to smother my weekend in a blanket of guilt? Where was she when I came home from school? She was busy rushing from beauty shop to bridge game, that's where. At night, while she was at the club or off to symphony, my father warmed us with hugs and bedtime stories. I cuddled deep into his nubby sweater safe from the bugaboos of childhood and my mother's icy disapproval.

"Yes. She and Mark deserve each other," I say. My words drip disgust. "They can sit around the fire at night and discuss the stock market while Abbey knits woollies. He'll go jogging, she'll toss tofu salads and they'll live happily ever after, Mommy and Daddy to my babies. Where the hell is that spaghetti?"

"Mothering isn't a thing you schedule between appointments the way you try to do, Jessica. It won't work that way and you know it."

She wipes my breakfast crumbs from the kitchen table.

"Did you know it, Mother? Did you? I can't recall that you did. You better hurry or you'll miss your movie or whatever you were going to do after you stopped in here to throw a few daggers at me. Jody, stop your screaming and kiss your grandma good bye. She's leaving."

My mother storms out the door. I look at the presents I've bought. They litter the floor, half in, half out of their boxes. The children ignore them. They watch television, bored and hungry. I pause. I've seen this same scene before. I lived it when I waited for my mother to take a minute to mother me. I remember the desolation; the need I couldn't express. I, too, dropped candy on the floor and begged for my favorite food.

Yes. I remember.

I return to the kitchen. The pizza is burned. The spaghetti sticks to a boiled out pot. "The hell with it," I say. "The hell with it all."

I take a deep breath. I smile. "Tuna fish? What a good idea, Jody. Let's all three make it together."

"Me, too?" asks Ben.

"Sure, you too." I laugh. "It won't taste as good if you don't help."

Jody cuts up the olives and Ben stirs in the mayonnaise. I boil and slice the eggs. We tease and laugh and make a sloppy, splattered mess together. After dinner, we sit in my only chair. Ben nestles deep in my lap and Jody cuddles in my arms. "Once upon a time, there was a little girl named Jody and she had a baby brother named Ben."

"Oh, Mommy," laughs Jody. "That's not once upon a time! That's us!"

The telephone rings. It is my lawyer. "Yes, Jessica. What's your emergency?"

I rub my chin in Jody's golden hair. I feel Ben's warmth in my lap and smell his baby freshness.

"Never mind," I say. "Everything is fine now. Just fine."

Christmas in July

If summer's here, can
Santa Claus be far behind?
- Shelley & Lynn Ruth

In the mid seventies, I lived in a mobile home in just outside Toledo, Ohio. Winter usually begins immediately after Halloween in that part of the Midwest, and the place is buffeted by storms without mercy until Memorial Day. One December, the wind and snow were so overwhelming that helicopters were flying food into those of us isolated in the country and the only vehicles on the road were tractors and Mack Trucks. That Christmas, I awoke early because the water pipes had frozen and the furnace was dead. The temperature inside my home was below freezing and I feared hypothermia if I didn't keep moving. When I managed to scrape the frost off my window and survey the holiday landscape, my carport had disappeared.

At seven o'clock that morning while I was trying to melt water on the propane heater to brush my teeth, my mother called me to wish me a joyous Noel. "What did Santa bring you this morning, Lynn Ruth?" she asked.

I scowled into the telephone. "I don't know what he brought me because The Red Cross hasn't arrived, but I know what he's taken away."

"Now, now," chided my mother from her warm suburban home. "Where is your Christmas spirit? I heard on the news they decorated the emergency planes with holly and mistletoe. You're in for a real treat!"

"I'd settle for a thaw," I said.

When I managed to hack away the ice that sealed the front door and push the dog outside to take care of his personal needs, I located the missing carport. The wind had swept it up to the roof. The next morning, I called my insurance company and my agent promised to send out an adjuster. That very afternoon, I heard the roar of a four wheel drive in first gear, and saw a caricature of Happy the Dwarf scamper up what should have been my front walk. I opened the door and the wind rushed into the hall knocking over a chair in my living room. My caller removed his hat and shook the thick globules of snow from his shoulders. He stomped the slush off his boots and held out his hand. "Hey!" he exclaimed. "I'm Oscar Brown, your insurance adjuster. I've come to look at the damage dear Mother Nature did to your little home."

“Yes,” I said. “Won’t you come in?”

“Oh, no!” he said. “I haven’t time. We have been inundated with calls this morning!”

His face become almost tragic and his voice caught as he spoke. “An awful lot of good folk had a very sad Christmas this year.”

He paused and smiled. “But I’m here to fix all that!” he exclaimed. “You just go about your business while I do my inspection.”

“It’s ten below zero out there,” I said. “Wouldn’t you rather I just described them to you? You see the carport . . . “

His hand hushed me. “I’m trained to detect every shred of damage covered by your policy,” he said. “Believe me, I have your interest at heart! I won the customer satisfaction award last year, and I mean to do it again.”

I had dealt with insurance adjusters before and this male Pollyanna couldn’t fool me. “I’ll bet you did,” I said.

He nodded. “They gave me a framed certificate,” he said. “It’s the first time I ever won anything. I was very proud. I’ll be right back.”

I watched him through the window as he plunged into drifts of snow and then popped up like a romping polar bear. He took out a pad of paper and began to write rapidly with mittened fingers and even from the distance of the kitchen window, I could see that he was whistling.

After almost an hour, he knocked at my door. “You had a great deal of damage here,” he said. “Your roof looks weakened and I think it should be reinsulated. The skirting is gone from the west side of the place and there are two cracked windows at the back.”

“Those windows cracked last year,” I said. “And the roof has never been right.”

He patted my shoulder. “I didn’t hear that,” he said. “Well, I must be off. You cannot imagine the paper work I have to do!”

The remainder of that winter was peppered with disaster. My appliances broke down during the next storm because of recurring power surges and when I telephoned to price new ones, I realized I would have to find over a thousand dollars to replace them. At the end of January, the wood support on my couch cracked from the tremendous fluctuation of temperatures and I called an upholsterer to repair it. He offered to bolster the sofa and repair the collapsed legs on two of my chairs for five hundred dollars. By the time I had dealt with these crises, it was June first and winter ended as abruptly as it had begun.

I still had heard nothing from sweet Oscar Brown. I wasn’t surprised. I’d been told horror stories of people who waited over ten years for money to repair storm damage. Still, I had to get my carport replaced before winter attacked and my neighbor offered to buy a prepackaged carport at Sears and install it for me for one hundred dollars.

I arranged to have new appliances delivered and made an appointment with the upholsterer to fix the damaged furniture. "I want to do the repairs before we have another winter freeze," I explained. "Once we have that Halloween blizzard, no one can get in or out of town."

By this time, my creditors had become so insistent, I unplugged the telephone. I walked the dog to the mailbox and removed a pile of letters. I shuffled through them wondering how many times Zanzibar Appliances wanted to waste postage on me and there was a letter from the insurance company marked IMPORTANT DOCUMENT ENCLOSED.

I tore open the envelope and removed a check for $2148.36 and a note. "Merry Christmas!" it said and it was signed Oscar Brown.

How far that little candle throws his beams!
So shines a good deed in a naughty world.
- Shakespeare

The Laundry Evolution

Housekeeping ain't no joke
- Louise May Alcott

Every time you change your underwear someone has to wash it, iron it, fold it and put it away. During our formative years, that person was our mother and for some of us, it still is. The average housewife with even a modicum of hygiene will do about fourteen loads of laundry a week; more if she has a large family. Nowadays, getting the job done is a matter of carting the dirty clothes into the laundry room, separating it into whites, colors and disgustingly filthy, dumping one pile into a washing machine, pouring in suitable amounts of soap, bleach, spot removers and softeners, setting the timer and pushing Start.

Some forty minutes later, the laundress must return, transfer the first load into a dryer after removing the all-cotton clothing to air dry. She will stuff the remainder into a dryer, set the timer and shove the colored clothing into the emptied washer, again set the timer, push start and run back to her inside chores for another forty minutes.

At this point, she returns to the laundry room to remove the whites to be folded, reset the dryer to permanent press, again separate the delicates, dump the rest in the dryer, push a button and address the really nasty pile. She will change the temperature setting and water level, put the clothes in with immense amounts of bleach, stain killers and a lethal detergent, push that button and hurry back inside to figure out how to accommodate the different diets of her hungry family. By the time she organizes a balanced meal for her vegetarian, a digestible one for the two year old, something that won't give her teenager diabetes and an exotic dish to remind her husband that he is special, the drier buzzer sounds and she is back in the laundry room folding the colored clothing, stuffing the now gleaming work clothes into the dryer.

A routine like this might kill a morning but it is a piece of cake compared to what my grandmother did in the 1920's. Sunday night, she separated the family's dirty clothes into whites, colors and the unrecognizable, and put kindling in the wood stove in the wash house to light the next morning. The wash house was a small shed just outside the back door with a big stove and three immense three legged laundry tubs.

On Monday morning, my grandmother was up at five so she could start the laundry water, then go into the kitchen to boil water for washing and cooking. She set the table, mixed the batter for biscuits, set out the eggs and bacon, mixed oats and water in a large pan to simmer and she returned to the laundry. She hauled the pot of boiling water outside and poured it into the first laundry tub. She added Crystal White Soap and the pile of white clothes. She stirred the mixture with an old broomstick and rubbed the bad spots on a rub board to get them out.

While the clothes were simmering, she hurried back into the kitchen to set the table, start the bacon and cover the porridge so it wouldn't get gummy. She shoved the biscuits into the oven and returned to the wash house. She filled the second tub with cold water, transferred the white clothes into it and boiled the colored clothes in the same water she had used for the first batch. She hurried back to the kitchen to save her biscuits and fry the eggs. She dished out the porridge with plenty of fresh butter and jam from last year's strawberries.

While her family gobbled up this immense repast guaranteed to give them early heart attacks, endless embolisms, diabetes and a cholesterol count in the thousands, she galloped back into the wash house to remove the colored clothes from the wash water and boil the jeans and work clothes. She wrung the water out of the whites and transferred them to the third tub now filled with cold water she had dragged from the pump just outside the back door. Then she hurried back inside to clear the table, send her children off to school and her husband to work.

She returned to the laundry stove to boil the starch until it clabbered and pray it wouldn't get lumps or she'd have to start over. She dipped the white clothes in the starch, wrung them out and carried them outside. She wiped off the lines strung across the back yard and hung them to dry. She ran back into the wash house, wrung the water out of the colored clothes, dipped them in the starch liquid, dumped the work clothes into the clean rinse water, emptied the soapy water into the vegetable garden, hung the colored clothes and rinsed the jeans in the second tub of water.

She returned to the house to do the breakfast dishes and make the beds and then rushed outside to wring out the work clothes and hang them on the line. By late afternoon, the clothes were dry enough and she managed to get the sheets off the line without dragging them into the grass very much. She folded them and put them between the mattresses and springs of the beds so they'd be pressed when it was time for her change the beds on Wednesday morning. She took down the rest of the clothes and sprinkled them for the next day's ironing, finished dusting, set the table and started the soup for dinner.

The next day after her usual morning routines, she put five or six irons on the kitchen stove to heat and tested them with spit to see if they were hot enough. She wiped the bottom of each iron with a cloth to get the soot off and created an ironing surface by covering the kitchen table with a quilt. Just when she finished ironing the last shirt, my mother, her three sisters and her brother came trooping into the house demanding cookies and milk. "First change into your play clothes," my grandmother would say. "And put the dirty ones in the laundry hamper."

Hooray for progress! Today's mothers accomplish procedure in two leisurely hours. In fact, all their housework has been simplified. Now, they have time for community service, car pooling and a job outside the home. The only task they haven't streamlined is the time it takes to become a mother. It still takes them nine months to make a baby.

Doesn't it?

There is as much dignity in doing laundry as writing a poem
- Booker T. Washington & Lynn Ruth

Another Dream

When we lose the right to be different,
We lose the privilege to be free.
- Charles Evans

Martin Luther King shared his dream of equality for us all, one hot summer day in 1963 and we have come a long way toward making that dream come true. But in our zeal to bestow equal opportunity on all mankind, I wonder if we have compromised another inalienable right: the privilege to be different.

I will never forget another even hotter summer day in 1980, in Wimberly, Texas, peopled by out of sync angels who rejected conformity because it insisted they wear shoes. All of us loved to sing Bible songs, share potluck dinners created from found items and work to make our world a happy place. Not one of us fit any stereotype known to man and none of us cared.

I was housed in a fifth wheel trailer on a ranch just outside of town. I fed two horses and a donkey for the owners of the place in exchange for hooking up to their utilities and using their laundry facilities. I lived with two dogs, one cat and an exhausted air conditioner, barely able to move air much less cool it. The heat that summer was so intense that clothes became a distressing liability. I elasticized a light blue, flowered pillowslip and wore that as a survival measure when the two dogs and I walked the country roads. Every morning, Mark Croy would knock on my door and say, "Hey, Lynn Ruth" which meant: "Put on your shoes honey, it's time to get going."

Mark was in his early twenties, well over six feet tall and I am just an inch over five feet. Mark wore a ragged straw hat he found in the dumpster outside K-Mart, no shoes and jeans that had seen better days on shorter legs. I was decked out in a fresh pillowslip and tennies. We were often mistaken for Ed Sullivan's Old Gold pack and matches before they got dressed for their commercial.

As we walked, we discussed the remote possibility of a breeze coming our way, the inequalities of rich and poor and where Mark could sleep that night. We turned to the right on the main road and stopped at Martha and Jonah's place for some sun tea and a dip in the stream while we pondered the immense changes in weather that had taken place over the century and marveled that all the birds weren't roasted. Mark swung high in the air in the tire that hung from the oak tree out front and Martha showed me how she had created a loaf of bread out of a yogurt starter, alfalfa seeds and ground acorns. We buttered the crumbling slices with honey from Jonah's hive and washed it down with sassafras tea.

Martha would say how lucky Mark was that his underwear was intact because his jeans were in tatters and Mark would reply that he preferred a breeze through his legs in heat like this. That inspired another round of tea, more seed bread and speculation on God's plan for the Texas hills since it had been months since a breeze had been detected anywhere at all.

Martha and Jonah called their dog Biff and we all continued toward town until we came to the Blue Hole. "Let's take a dip in the quarry," Mark would say and down we would climb to the only place in town where we could cool off.

As soon as we descended, Mark jumped into the quarry and Rachel McGinnis poured pump water over my head to relieve me. I shook the drips from my shoulders and went inside to Luke and Becky stories they refused to believe about midwestern snow storms. As soon as the children's eyes drooped, Rachel kissed them good night and Mark joined me to go back to the main road with Martha, Jonah, Rachel and her husband Abraham. When we hit the main road, we hitched a ride with Mary Lou Redd who drove large expensive cars and did the books for her daddy in San Marcos, the biggest town near us. Mary Lou had a daughter named Shauna who was so beautiful she didn't have to do anything but stand on a corner to attract everything like flies to butter. Mary Lou also had a son no one discussed and three immense white dogs known for their determination to catch the moon even in sunlight. She dropped us off at the Sunset Market to get provisions and went home to work her crosswords puzzles. "You coming to church later?" I called and she shook her head. "We're Methodists," she explained.

Mark and I bought what we thought we could carry and then continued until we got to the post office where old Mrs. Atlee sat sorting what mail there was and putting it into post office boxes. As soon as we entered the door, her face flooded with smiles and she stood up, hugged us both and gave the dogs fresh bowls of water. "Ain't it HOT?" she exclaimed and we nodded. She opened her fridge, poured us some iced tea (chamomile) and pointed to a platter of blueberry muffins that still had the aroma of the oven about them. "Fresh this morning," she would say. "Y'all just help yourselves," and we all did.

The rest of the afternoon varied from visits to Belinda's Beauty Shop to trim the hair from the all our eyes including the two dog's, to stopping at the Health Emporium for a sprout sandwich and more liquid to wash away the heat inside us. If it was Monday, Wednesday or Sunday, we all gathered in a condemned warehouse that we called church to sing and love each other. If it was Saturday, we went over to the girls' camp to watch outdoor movies. The Drive In was owned by two women who lived in a log cabin behind the big screen and kept two horses in their living room. "I don't like them rooting around in all that grit out back," explained Cassandra Stark. "This way, we got control."

The movies were reruns of old forties films and that year I saw Yankee Doodle Dandee, Random Harvest, and Gaslight twenty three times. We also saw Going My Way, but only once.

On Tuesdays, we all went on a hayride out at Christopher Murphy's farm and on Thursdays we did choir practice. That always puzzled me. "Who listens to the choir?" I asked Martha. "It seems like were all in it."

" I guess the Lord is the one who listens to us," said Martha. "What do you think?"

I didn't answer that one; I just threw back my shoulders, prayed my pillowslip would stay in place while I sang. "AMAZING GRACE!!!!" we roared and indeed our grace was heady wine for us all. Every singer's melody blended together to produce the most thrilling music I had ever heard. Together, we showed the rest of the world the immense difference one person's song can make in the quality of life's chorus. I was in that choir twenty-one years ago and the music we made that summer replays in my heart whenever I forget that each of us is a gift to the universe, a gift that makes the entire world an exciting place for us all.

What one man can do is
change the world and make it right again . . .
Ain't it great what one man can do?
- John Denver

The Acting Fiasco

Acting is a masochistic form of exhibitionism.
- Laurence Olivier

The first time I appeared on stage was at summer camp in Maine when I was twelve years old. I played a gambler who crooned, "You've Got That Look." to my beloved. On the day of the performance, an atavistic mosquito landed in my eye, and I appeared on stage in dark glasses that reflected the spotlights with so much heat that the object of my affection suffered third degree burns and had to be carted off the stage.

My next venture into the world of drama was in college. I was to sing "I'm a Little Teapot" in appropriate costume. The cup, the saucer and the pourer were on stage when I was suddenly overcome with a severe cramp that reduced me to an agonized heap, paper mache spout and all. The cup remained empty, but the pourer had excellent stage presence and improvised "You're the Cream in my Coffee".

I changed my major to Education.

It was another ten years before I ventured behind the lights once more. This time, I was part of a fledgling Community Theater Group desperate for participants. I had just had a divorce and the director, who knew my parents, managed to convince my mother that if I played the lead, it would enhance my opportunity to meet husband #3. Although I was approaching thirty, I still felt compelled to obey my mother and I was at every rehearsal on time.

The man who played my lover in this drama was my dentist in real life and the villain of the piece was a darling innocent we nicknamed Buckets Bershon for obvious reasons. I invited all my first graders to opening night and they sat in the front row waving and whistling as the curtain rose. I appeared clad in a spectacular dress and my Aunt Sally's mink cape. My dentist kissed me before I had a chance to say a word, and while I was gasping from his ardent embrace, Buckets Bershon hit me on the head with a rifle butt and locked me in a steel cabinet. He turned swiftly and aimed his weapon at my dentist. From this incident, the plot evolved. I did not return to the stage until the end of the last act when my dentist managed to convince the authorities that Buckets belonged behind bars. My hero rushed to the cabinet, dynamited the lock, I emerged and we embraced. At that point, I was to say my only line: "DAHLING!". However, the cabinet was very stuffy and I had been in it for two hours, Instead of returning his embrace, I fainted and the director called 911.

That ended my stage career until this summer when I decided to study drama with a professional. There were 14 of us in the class and every one of the participants could memorize lines in an instant and extemporize on call. For our final session, each of us performed one monologue and one scene. My classmates seemed to need no coaching because of their unbelievable natural ability. I wrote out all my speeches several times, recited them at coffee houses, on BART, in doctors' offices and while bathing. Still, I could not remember one word or gesture once I stood before the class. "You'll do fine once you're on stage," said my teacher.

I recalled my previous stage fiascoes and drank a gallon of Ginkgo before I addressed my scripts once more. My monologue was easy because all I had to do was speak to a corpse, but the assigned scene presented immense difficulties for me. Brynn Kramer and I were to perform a dialogue from "Agnes of God." Brynn was an optimistic college student who hoped to take to the stage and forget exams forever when we graduated from our drama tutoria. She was to play the young innocent Agnes and I was supposed to be the cold, professional therapist. I blanked out every time we rehearsed but I did manage to remember that if I forgot a phrase all I had to do was grab Brynn's hand and shout "Agnes, You are a mistake" to trigger a long monologue from my partner.

For our final examination, the members of the workshop gathered on stage to perform. I glanced out into the audience and THERE WAS JOHN PANTOLEON the director my local theater group. I had absolutely no doubt that once the man saw my performance, he would insist on launching a series of one woman shows for me and offer me a series of starring roles for the winter season season.

I was first on the program because the teacher had enough wisdom to know that in good theater one saves the best for last. I stood behind those lights for my monologue and looked down at what was supposed to be my dead husband. I cleared my throat, straightened my shoulders and shouted "WALTER! LOOK ME IN THE EYE!!!

"He's dead," hissed the teacher.

Brynn and I were next and my only hope was that our piece would save my day. I was supposed say the first line. I looked at Brynn and all the words I had tried to memorize froze in my throat. I managed to remember the one phrase guaranteed to get a reaction and I shouted, "AGNES!!! I AM A MISTAKE!"

Brynn looked up with a shocked expression and cried, "NO! I am the mistake."

It was too much for both of us. I wrapped her in my arms and sobbed, “I think this whole thing was a mistake.”

The applause was deafening.

When the show was over, I met John Pantoleon in the lobby. Now, I know John Pantoleon and he is a very perceptive man. I was certain he would see my latent abilities despite the poor showing I made on stage. “Well, John,” I said. “How did you like my performance?”

John, whose tact is legendary, took my hand in his and looked deep into my eyes. “Well, said he. “You certainly had That Look.”

I blushed. “Yes,” I said. “I’ve had it since I was twelve years old.”

In theater, the audience wants to be surprised
. . .but the actors do not.
- Sad Experience

Rain

When I moved to California, I was amazed the way traffic is paralyzed when it rains. I am originally from the midwest and in my town, winter attacked us November first as regularly as if the Lord Himself were standing by with a stop watch. The humidity would rise to 99%, the temperature drop below zero and the snows descend. The roads were glaciers until promptly at dawn on May 31st, when the temperature rose to one hundred degrees. The humidity remained constant.

In winter, I can remember devoting the entire day to driving to the grocery store. I would bundle up in a storm coat, wrap several scarves around my body and pull on my stadium boots. I'd put the chains on my tires and careen out the driveway only to slither down the road two miles an hour with periodic stalls in snow drifts the size of Mt. Rainier. When I arrived at the store, there would be nothing on the shelves because the delivery trucks were stalled on the highway. I would make the journey back at an even slower pace because by evening the roads were clogged with wrecked vehicles and abandoned tractors who failed to do their job. The year we were snowbound for over a week and helicopters dropped food to us, I vowed to move to someplace bearable.

When I found the Bay Area, I discovered my brand of heaven. The first year I was here, the rain was never more than a casual downpour and I don't remember putting on a pair of boots or a heavy coat. However, in the winter of 1982, I got my first taste of the torrents that destroy tempers while they refill our reservoirs.

I was living in a tiny place about the size of the average disabled toilet stall and I had accumulated a large family of four footed friends. At that time, I had Jake, an overweight cocker spaniel who looked at me with adoring eyes and panted when he saw me the way I had always dreamed someone would at the Senior Prom. Cindy was a chocolate poodle so insecure, she jumped on my lap at every opportunity. She liked to rest her head against my heart to assure herself that it was beating. My third dog, Molly was afflicted with perpetual flatulence. Her very presence was enough to empty a room.

I also had three cats, Toby Ann, who had come to me from the wilds behind Menlo Park, Bertha, a tiny newcomer I had adopted in Oklahoma

City and Eileen, the only one who had endured the Midwest with me. We would listen to the frantic weather reports on KCBS and chuckle together.

I believe in walking my dogs every day. They need exercise and so do I. I had never encountered rain as pervasive as I did that winter but I refused to allow it to interfere with the health of my family. I purchased little yellow slickers for the dogs and an oversized golf umbrella to shield us all. On the first day of serious precipitation, I put on my waterproof rainsuit and rubber boots and leashed up everyone. When I opened my front door, a rush of water blew into my living room and knocked over the corner lamp. The outdoors looked like a filled bathtub and I could barely make out my own front step. I squared my shoulders and nodded to the dogs. "We're off!" I announced.

By the end of the week, nothing in my house was dry. Water leaked under the door and around the windows. It soaked the rug and it left immense puddles on the floor. My clothes had a film of mildew on them and even the cats looked moldy. Toby Ann insisted on maintaining her nightly prowls and her muddy footprints gave my ivory rug the look of a rejected abstract painting. Eileen was smart enough to sit on the couch and wait it out. She had been through a real winter. Bertha refused to use the litter box because she didn't want to get her feet wet. She adopted a corner of the living room rug to relieve herself and my home smelled like the cat house at the zoo.

My rain equipment was history before the first storm ended. Jake chewed through his raincoat because it was the color of his favorite rubber toy and Molly wiggled out of hers because she couldn't bear restraint. Cindy caught her nails in her jacket when she tried to jump upwards to do a routine check on my coronary condition. My rain boots sprung a leak when I stepped on an abandoned axle in the middle of the road and the golf umbrella reversed itself with such force that it almost flew me across the bay.

After a month of this new form of water sport, I looked as though I had just endured a ritual bath and the dogs resembled a strange variety of antelope when we walked down the street. On the day that finished my rain treks once and for all, the downpour had paused and I decided to risk running down to the post office before the next storm moved in. I had a week's correspondence and bills to mail.

I managed to put the dogs' dripping collars around their necks and get them leashed. They ran to the door, their enthusiasm undampened by the dreadful storms we had endured and we emerged to a relatively dry day. The dogs and I did our snake dance between puddles and I looked up at the sky. A cloud so black it resembled a bloated ink blot was sinking toward me at approximately the speed of light.

We managed to get to the end of the block before the sky opened up and a celestial waterfall emptied on my head. I picked up Cindy and shielded her under my jacket. She immediately nestled her head against my sweatshirt and played stethoscope. I couldn't protect the others because Jake weighed almost as much as I did and I didn't think I could endure Molly that close to my nose. She was emitting such immense volumes of gas that I could actually see it form blue clouds above her tail. Jake couldn't bear walking beside her. He yanked so violently at his leash that my arm felt like it was not long for its socket.

At this point, I rounded the corner to the post office and tried to fish my letters out from between Cindy and my shirt. Suddenly a tiny pink volkswagen drove up over the curb and screeched to a halt at my feet. The irate driver leaned her (dry) head out the window and screamed, "THOSE DOGS ARE SHIVERING!!! WHERE ARE THEIR RAIN COATS? I AM REPORTING YOU TO THE SPCA!"

As I turned to the woman, a gust of water blew into my mouth and Cindy relieved herself on my sweatshirt. I thought I was having a hot flash and couldn't believe menopause would dare to chose so inopportune a moment to begin. I narrowed my eyes and if looks could kill, I would have been able to toss that woman on the road and drive the Volkswagen home immediately. "YOU DO THAT,"I hissed. "AND CALL THE SENIOR HELP LINE AS WELL. IF I DON'T DIE OF PNEUMONIA FIRST, I AM MOVING TO RENO."

I managed to stuff my letters into the mailbox and the four of us paddled home. I turned the heater on high, gathered my dripping family in my arms and said to them, "Never again. Never AGAIN."

It has been raining a great deal this past year but when it does, my little pets and I remain inside. We all gather at the window and I say to my babies, "If that stuff were snow, we would be stuck with it until the end of May."

I play California Dreamin' on the stereo and we all begin to dance. We dance because the exercise is good for us. We dance to keep our spirits up and we dance because the rain is outside and we are not.

Santa's Messengers

I was born at the end of the depression when we treated strangers differently than we do today. In those days, people often knocked at our back door to ask for food and my mother always invited them inside for a hot bowl of soup or a sandwich. It was not that we were wealthy. No one had extra money in the early thirties. But we were not afraid to share what we had because we knew that one upset to our own budget and we, too, would not have enough to eat or a warm place to sleep.

One man appeared at our door several times a week. He was very different from most of the vagrants that sat at my mother's table because he refused to take anything for nothing. "Let me sweep the walk for you, Missus?" he'd say or "Why don't you let me hang out those sheets for you today?"

He was unshaven and wore drab, patched clothes obviously salvaged from the dustbin. He used to keep a potato in his mouth and when he smiled you could see it through the spaces between his tobacco stained teeth. He rolled it around in his mouth and tucked it behind his molars when he spoke. That was why we all called him Potato Tom.

He seemed to enjoy the tasks my mother gave him and did them with great energy. As winter approached, his clothes got shabbier and he wore no gloves or scarf to protect him from the relentless Ohio cold. His hands were spotted with reddened chilblains and as soon as he stood still, he shivered uncontrollably. "Would you like to borrow a coat, Tom?" Mama would ask. "You must be freezing. I have an old scarf we never wear. Let me give it to you."

He always smiled and shook his head. "I'm used to being outdoors, Missus," he'd say. "But a hot bowl of something would sure feel good right about now."

Tom was my very favorite of all the people who came to our door. I would sit across from him at the table and while he ate, he would tell me stories about places he'd been. "I remember one winter I spent in Floriday," he told me. "It was so hot there you never even needed a coat and you couldn't be hungry what with oranges and coconuts free for the picking. But then times got bad and I couldn't get work so I walked up north."

I looked at his torn shoes. The laces had disappeared long ago and he secured them to his feet with pieces of rope. "You walked all the way from Floriday?" I said. "Didn't your feet get tired?"

He shook his head. "In this life, honey, you do what you have to do. Ain't that right, Missus?" he asked my mother.

Mama's eyes looked very red and she sniffled like she had a cold. "I have some meat loaf from last night I could warm up for you, Tom," she said. "How does that sound?"

He was very polite when he ate and even though I was only four years old, I knew his manners were a lot better than mine. He never dropped food all over his clothes the way I did and he never forgot to wipe his mouth with a napkin. I took his hand when he left and I always said, "Come back, Tom and tell me about Floriday"

He would look over my head at my mother and then he'd nod. "Maybe later in the week, honey," he'd say. "When your mama needs some windows washed."

The year that Tom came to our house was when I found out what Santa Claus really meant. Even though we did not observe the religious ceremony of Christmas, I believed in the jolly benefactor with all my heart and had long, imaginary conversations with him weeks before the big day when my mother took me to LaSalle's to sit on Santa's lap.

As we walked through the slush and ice on the downtown streets, I noticed that every single corner had a Santa ringing his bell for people to contribute to The Salvation Army. Everyone one of these Santa's patted me on the head, and told me that my Christmas dreams would come true while my mother fished in her purse and pulled out a nickel to drop into their cast iron pots.

I didn't say anything when we met the first Santa but by the time we got to Adams and Madison, seven jolly gentlemen had promised me all the goodies I wanted for Christmas and I became suspicious. "Why are there so many Santas walking around the street?" I asked my mother. "I thought only one Santa came down the chimney Christmas night."

My mother gave me the answer mothers have always given observant children since Christmas began. "They are all Santa's helpers, Lynnie Ruth," she explained. "He is very busy this time of year getting everyone's gifts ready for Christmas Eve and he can't be everywhere in the world at once."

"I thought he was magic," I told my mother. "I thought he could do wondrous things."

"And he can," my mother assured me. "Just look how many people he has scattered across the globe telling boys and girls that their wishes will come true!"

"Does Santa tell all these helpers what to say?" I asked.

My mother nodded. "He sends them messages from his heart."

By this time we were in the department store on our way up to the fourth floor where the Real Santa sat on a red and green throne. I held my mother's hand and tried to be very quiet while we waited in line. When at last, it was my turn, I ran up the steps and jumped on the bearded man's lap. I looked into his eyes and I Saw Truth. "You're not Santa!" I cried and my eyes filled with tears of disappointment. "You're Potato Tom!"

From behind that beard came the voice I had heard so many times at my mother's kitchen table. "Today, I am your very own Santa Claus, Lynnie Ruth," he said. "Santa sent me down from the North Pole to tell you that he knew what a very good girl you are and he will bring you that Shirley Temple doll you want and a little stove that really works."

I was shocked. "How did you know I wanted all that?" I said.

Tom's eyes twinkled just like the picture books said they would and his pillow stuffed belly shook with laughter. "Why Santa told me!" he said.

I peered into his mouth. "What happened to your potato!" I asked. "I can't see it anymore."

"I got so excited when I saw you standing in line that I swallowed it!" he said.

"Then that's what I'll give YOU for Christmas," I said. "A brand new potato!" and I scrambled off his lap so I could give the next child a turn.

As we walked away I said to my mother, "How did Tom get to be Santa's helper? Did he walk to the North Pole like he did from Floriday. ?"

My mother shook her head and when she spoke I could barely understand her words because she was afflicted with a very sudden winter cold. "I guess he just looked up at the winter sky and asked God to help him help himself."

"You mean God told Santa Claus to hire Tom?" I asked.

My mother shook her head, "No, Lynn Ruth," she said. "God gave him nobility and that's the most important qualification for the job.

Anticipate charity by preventing poverty.
- Maimonides

The Power of Prayer

Little Sarah Jordan loved horses. She lived with her parents in the Texas Hill Country and every day, she begged her parents to buy her a horse. "A horse is a very big responsibility, Sarah," said her mother, Katherine. "Who would take care of it? I have to go to my job every day and I'm too busy to feed it and groom it when I get home."

"I will," promised Sarah. "I watch Nobbin for Mr. Murphy, don't I?"

Her mother laughed. "You feed that horse sugar and you pet him, honey," she said. "But there is a lot more to tending an animal than that. Maybe some day when you're grown up, you can handle that kind of responsibility, but right now, I think you're going to have to settle for dogs and cats."

That night, Sarah's Aunt Mary came over for dinner and the child shared her disappointment with the older woman. Mary nodded and said," If you really want a horse, honey, you have to pray for it. That's the best way for someone your age to get when she wants."

"Stop filling that child's head with false hope, Mary," snapped Katherine. "She could pray from now till next year and Mike and I won't be able to afford to buy her anything like that. And even if we could, who would walk it? Who would clean out its stable?"

Sarah ignored her mother and looked up at her aunt. "Really, Aunt Mary?" she asked. "If I prayed very hard and was as good as I can be, God will give me what I want?"

"It's certainly worth a try, honey," said her aunt.

She turned to her sister and shook her head. "It's not going to do her any harm to say a prayer for what she wants, Katherine," she said. "Beside, you never know if she'll get it."

Katherine was furious. "People pray to be strong or wise, Mary," she said. "They pray for understanding and the ability to select the best course in their lives. They don't ask for dolls and horses or new dresses. That cheapens the whole idea of God."

"I don't think so," said her sister. "I think prayer is a very healthy thing. Do you want me to help you set the table?"

For the next several months, Sarah Jordan prayed for a horse before every meal and when she went to bed, but nothing happened. The next time Mary came over to visit, she said, "All this praying is a waste of time, Aunt Mary. "It's been such a long time and I still don't have my horse."

Mary took the little girl in her arms. "Honey, God gets lots of very important requests all the time," she said. "You can't expect him to put your dreams ahead of the needs that people have for homes and proper medical care. He'll get to you as soon as he can, if you just don't lose faith."

"MARY!" said Katherine. "If you keep this up, that kid is going to be so disillusioned, she'll abandon religion before she's ten years old."

"Maybe," said Mary. "But at least she isn't pestering you about it anymore."

Katherine laughed. "That's a point," she said.

About six months after this conversation, John Murphy knocked on the Jordan door while Sarah was in school. "Katherine," he said. "I have a favor to ask you. Joan and I are moving to a smaller place in Austin and we need to find a good home for Nobbin. He's too old to sell, but he's a wonderful animal, almost a member of our family. Sarah has been telling me about all that praying she's been doing and we thought perhaps you would let her have the horse when we move."

Katherine shook her head. "I'd love to help you out, John," she said. "But where would we put the animal? Our yard doesn't even have a fence, much less a stable. Horses are expensive to keep up and I don't think we can afford the food and vet bills right now."

"Nobbin is a very old horse, Katherine," said John Murphy. "He doesn't need that much exercise anymore. Jane and I are prepared to pay his expenses as long as he lives and we'll even build you a fence from those old boards I have out back. Your little girl can give him all the love and grooming he needs."

Katherine closed her eyes for a moment and saw her daughter kneeling with bowed head before every meal. "If you will help us with expenses, I think I can talk Mike into doing it," she said.

John smiled. "You won't be sorry, Katherine," he promised. "Nobbin is a gentle animal and he loves your daughter as much as she loves him."

When Sarah's school bus dropped her off that afternoon, the child ran into the house and dropped her books on the table. "Is there any milk and cookies?" she asked.

Katherine nodded and Sarah sat down at the table. She clasped her hands together and bowed her head. Katherine brought a glass of milk to the little girl and she smiled. "You need to say thank you in your prayer today, honey," she said "Mr. Murphy is going to move to Austin and he wants you to give you Nobbin when he leaves."

The little girl's face erupted in smiles. "Did you say yes, Mom?" she asked. "I know I can do a good job. Mr. Murphy has shown me how to feed him and everything."

Katherine nodded. "We'll talk to Daddy about it tonight," she said. "But I think he'll say okay."

"Can I run over to Mr. Murphy's to bring Nobbin home now?" asked Sarah.

Katherine shook her head. "We have to wait until Mr. Murphy builds us a fence and a place for the horse to sleep," she said.

Sarah jumped up from the table and ran to the telephone. "I can't wait to tell Aunt Mary!" she said.

When her aunt answered the phone, the child cried, "Aunt Mary! Aunt Mary! God finally heard me! I got a horse!"

"That's marvelous, honey," said Mary. "I'll come over to see it as soon as I finish dinner."

Sarah shook her head at the receiver. "He's not here yet," she said.

"Why not?" asked Mary.

Sarah's eyes filled with tears. "I forgot to pray for a fence," she said.

Will Power

Necessity is not a fact, but an interpretation.
- Nietzsche

When I was fourteen years old, I worked at an afternoon day care center for disadvantaged youth. This was a shocking experience for me because many of the children were from families that had escaped Nazi Germany and others knew poverty that I never realized existed. I was often reduced to tears when I saw a child in a tattered shirt or realized his lunch was totally inadequate for a growing body. I watched over these children like a mother hen and tried to protect them from harm.

And I loved them. I found excuses for their rude and often abusive behavior because I was furious at an unjust world that could be so brutal to needy and innocent children. I had plenty to eat and lived in a warm, beautiful house. Why shouldn't they?

My favorite child was a six year old named Brian Gilman. He was small and dark and he often wore the same unwashed jeans for days at a time. I could actually identify stains from the juice and cookies we served him days before on his shirt and pants. Brian's mother could barely speak English because the family had only been in this country a few months. She worked long hours as part of a custodial team so her children were alone most of the day. The father had been slaughtered by the Nazis. Brian had some kind of muscular degenerative disease and his leg was in a brace. He was a wild, adventurous child and difficult to control, but his spirit and determination to participate in every activity despite his handicap delighted me. When everyone played hide 'n seek, no one could find him and he flew fast as the wind when they all played tag.

I was working for an austere realist whose name was Sadie Brown and I hated her. She was a short, stocky woman with dark hair tied back into a bun. She dressed in starched white blouses and dark skirts and stood apart from the group surveying them as if they were animals in a cage. She pulled away as if stung if a child dared to touch her hand. She was a rigid disciplinarian and it seemed to me she had no understanding of the irresistible impulses of youth. There was no softness in her; no love for the children under her care. I had never seen her smile and if a child was injured, she ignored his wail of pain and walked away from the noise.

We were both out on the playground one day, when I looked up to see Brian trying to climb the ladder of the slide. His braces clattered on the steps and he forced his arms to propel him to the top. I gasped and ran to stop the child but Mrs. Brown restrained me. "Leave him alone," she said.

I looked at her with all the hatred I had suppressed during the long months of working for her. "He'll break his leg if tries to maneuver that narrow slide with a brace on his foot," I hissed. "I've got to stop him."

She tightened her grip. "Let him try," she said. "If he succeeds, he won't be afraid to experiment with other ways to use his legs. If he can't manage, we'll be right here to catch him. Should you stop him from forcing those leg muscles of his to become stronger, they'll atrophy and he will indeed be crippled for the rest of his life."

"He is going to break his neck going down that thing," I said. "And it will be your fault."

Still her hand restrained me. "Watch," she said.

I kept my eyes on the struggling child certain that this woman had allowed him to become permanently maimed. The little boy inched himself to the top of the structure and forced his cumbersome limbs into the narrow decline. He slid down to the bottom and ran over to the sandbox, filled with his new sense of power. He was triumphant and so was Sadie Brown.

It was in that very long moment as I watched a child descend to what I thought would be his death, that I realized the immense power of the human will. That child accomplished what he wanted to do because he was determined that nothing would stop him. His determination propelled him into a one success after another. He was out of his braces by the time he was ten. He went on to become a star athlete and an honor student. He is now a successful lawyer who barely remembers those years when everyone but Sadie Brown thought he would be an invalid for life.

I worked with children for many years after that and never again did I try to restrain anyone from insisting his reach exceed his grasp. It is obvious to me that our only real handicaps are those we give ourselves and the dreams that fail are those we fear to pursue.

Where willingness is great
The difficulties cannot be great
- Machiavelli

Memorial Day - 1943

When I was nine years old, Masako Nakano came to our house to take care of my sister and me. Masako was a Nisei who had been sent to the Heart Mountain Internment Camp from Fresno where her family had prospered until the outbreak of the Second World War. She had just earned her master's degree in education and because of the relocation of Japanese Americans, she was unable to begin her teaching career. When my parents opened our home to her, I became her first class and I have never had a teacher more dedicated or more beloved.

Memorial Day of that year, my mother and her sisters decided to plant a community victory garden in my Aunt Tick's backyard, because it was the biggest one in the family. Masako said she would help us make a vegetable patch guaranteed to grow . "At home, we always had a celebration after we finished our spring planting," she said. "Wouldn't it be fun for us to do that ,too?"

"Did you have a feast with drums and circle dancing?" I asked

"Not exactly," said Masako. "We just shared a meal and then all the children put on a variety show."

"I really love to sing and dance." I said. "But I don't always carry a tune."

"Just listen to your heart, Lynnie Ruth," said Masako. "That's how the most beautiful music happens."

We called our production "A Celebration of America" and invited my cousins to take part. "Sing something from your heart," I explained. "Masako will do the rest."

"My favorite song is "The Strip Polka," I told Masako. "I know all the words to it."

Masako hesitated. "Do you know what the singer is doing while she sings?" she asked.

I nodded. "She's taking off her clothes," I said. "Obviously she is performing in a very hot room."

Another pause. "Right," said Masako.

For the next week, Masako was so busy she didn't have time to miss her family. My mother had saved lots of ration coupons and she and Masako planned a menu filled with all the things our family loved to eat. The day before the picnic they frosted my mother's five egg chocolate cake with red, white and blue frosting and I helped decorate it with American flags. When Masako wasn't chopping up potatoes for the salad or searching for recipes that didn't use too many ration points, she helped me rehearse my song. "It's going to be very hard to shake my shoulders and swivel my hips if I have to wear a lot of clothes," I said.

"Why not wear your bathing suit draped with lots of pretty scarves?" said Masako. "I'll play the um pah pahs on the piano and yell, 'Here comes Queenie'. That will be your cue to start singing."

Memorial Day dawned wet and gloomy as it always does in my hometown. "We won't be able to do our planting!" I wailed.

"Nothing important is ever easy," said Masako. "Close your eyes and will the sun to shine for us. You have three hours."

At noon, the sun peeped through the clouds. "It worked!" "I exclaimed.

Masako smiled at me. "Thanks to you."

"Glad to do it," I said.

A few minutes later, everyone followed Masako out to the backyard. She handed my aunts spades and shovels and my cousins' packets of seed. "Try to make the earth very soft," she said. "Be sure the seeds are well covered or the wind will blow them away."

"I don't want to plant green peppers," said Leonard. "I want to do radishes."

"Here, Leonard," I said and I handed him my packet of seeds. "I'll do green peppers instead."

We all started digging and planting while Aunt Tick's dog Pee Wee galloped through the mud. "Can't someone tie up that dog?" asked Leonard.

Masako shook her head. "This is a project for the entire family," she said. "He's helping us more than you think. These lumps of clay are very dense."

When the seeds were planted, Masako gave each of us bright colored markers for each vegetable. Then we strung crepe paper across the patio and put out little flags for my baby cousins to wave during the Big Show. By that time it was five o'clock. We put out the food and everyone ate like there wasn't a war going on. When we had all gorged ourselves on cake and ice cream, the grown ups sat down to watch the entertainment. My cousins and I lined up at the kitchen door. "I want to go first," said Leonard. "I am going to sing 'Praise the Lord and Pass the Ammunition.' I brought my be-be gun so I could shoot it to make the song more convincing."

Masako shook her head. "That's a lovely idea, Leonard, but shooting guns is too dangerous. You might hurt someone. "

Leonard's eyes filled with tears. "We can all shout 'Bang Bang' when you come out, Leonard," I said.

"It won't be the same," said Leonard.

Masako patted his hand. "You picked such a good song, we'd like you to finish the program. We need something really rousing for our finale. Lynnie and I have planned a lovely number to open the festivities and you can clap and dance with us."

Leonard' s face turned purple and he ran to his Mother. "I don't have to listen to you," he shouted. "You're a Jap."

The silence was so heavy it felt like someone had dropped a lead sheet over our heads. Masako's eyes filled with tears and her head was bowed over the piano. I ran to her and threw my arms around her. "She's Masako!" I said and I too was crying. "And you could never have had this picnic if she hadn't done all the work."

That was when my father decided to take over. "Memorial Day is the time that we honor our heroes," he said. " And Masako's whole family are our heroes today. Her brother is fighting in Europe to defeat the enemy and she taught us how to plant a garden so our farmers can send more food to the boys overseas."

"And she showed us how to find the music in our hearts," I said.

Masako wiped her eyes and played some chords on the piano. "It's time to begin the show!" she announced. "Here comes Queenie!"

The Way It Was - 1927

The year was 1927 and my mama was a senior at Woodward High School in Toledo, Ohio. My Uncle Charlie was a junior, Aunt Hazel was a freshman and my little Aunt Tick was still in grade school. That was the year my grandpa moved the outdoor plumbing inside and installed a real bathtub with hot water from a tap. Before that, everyone used to bathe in a big washtub my grandma filled with heated water on the stove. The first one in got clean hot water and my little Aunt Tick always got stuck with a cold bath because she was the baby. When my grandpa built that bathroom, her personal hygiene improved one hundred percent.

Charles Lindbergh was a national hero that year. He flew non stop from New York to Paris in 33 and 1/3 hours and the whole country was so proud of him that they named a dance after him: THE LINDY HOP.

That was the dance my mother and her sisters practiced every afternoon in their living room on Baker Street. The girls rolled back the rug and pushed the furniture to one side of the room. Mama took out the latest Louis Armstrong or Wayne King record and my Aunt Hazel wound up the victrola. Uncle Charlie pulled out some of my grandma's pots from the shelf under the sink and pretended he was the drummer. My little Aunt Tick would start tapping her feet and wiggling her bottom even before the music began. She was adorable with a head full of ringlets and so many freckles no one could tell where her skin began. She did a lot of giggling and no one could resist hugging her to pieces.

The minute that music started, the neighborhood kids ran up the porch steps to join in the dance. Everyone did the lindy while Uncle Charlie beat those pots 'til they had so many dents my grandma had to buy new ones to make her famous chicken soup. My mama loved to truck on down and my Aunt Hazel shimmied as if her bones were made of Jell-O. She was the best dancer on the block and when she did the Charleston, her feet blurred like spokes on a wheel.

Jackie Green used to run over to my grandma's house as soon as he finished delivering his papers just to watch my Aunt Hazel cut a rug. She spun on her toes so fast her skirt flew right up around her waist and if Jackie was lucky he got a good look at her bloomers. "That boy has a dirty mind," warned my mother, but my Aunt Hazel was the wild one of the family and she didn't care.

My daddy was very in love with my mother even then but she paid no attention to him because he was boring. Mama only had eyes for Frank Silverstein who lived right down the street. He was such a smooth dancer that his glasses never even slipped down his nose when he did the Suzie Q. My father was very stubborn and he was sure that if he really put his mind to it, he could win my mama's heart even though he had two outsized left feet and his glasses were always sliding down his nose and into his dinner plate. He wrote Mama long, passionate love letters but she just threw them in the trash along with her used ticket stubs and empty candy wrappers.

My mama was a pushover for popular music was always singing hit songs like "I'm Lookin' Over a Four Leaf Clover and "Blue Skies Smilin' at Me and even though my daddy was tone deaf, he tried to sing along with her so she would begin to love him. One of the hits that year was "Ida, Sweet as Apple Cider" by Red Nichols. My mama loved that song best of all because Ida was her name. My daddy used to serenade her with it when he came over to dance with her, but it didn't do him a bit of good. "You might know the words, Izzy," my mama would say. "But I can't make any sense out of the tune."

On Saturday afternoons, the gang gathered in Mama's living room to listen to a rebroadcast of Duke Ellington's brand new radio program from the Cotton Club in New York City. His hit record that year was "Creole Love Call" with Adelaide Hall singing the vocal. She made her voice sound just like one of the instruments in the orchestra. My mama had a very pretty voice and she used to imitate Adelaide Hall but she just couldn't get it right. "That's because you don't sing soprano," said my daddy.

My mama smiled at him when he said that but she still loved Frank Silverstein best. My daddy had pimples on his face and he had a terrible sense of rhythm. Frank Silverstein actually shaved with a razor he sharpened with a leather strap. He was almost a man.

My little Aunt Tick was very shy and when all the high school boys started jumping around in the living room, she ran into the bathroom and shut the door. She would take off her shoes and practice her dancing in the bathtub. One afternoon, Harry Marks from Putnam Street came over with my Daddy to dance with the girls. My grandma served lots of lemonade to everyone and pretty soon, Harry had to use that brand new indoor facility my Grandpa installed.

He pushed open the door and there was my little Aunt Tick in the bathtub doing The Black Bottom for all she was worth. She was singing "I'm Looking Over a Four Leaf Clover" at the top of her lungs and smacking her heels with her hands.

Harry took one look at her and lost his heart right there in the bathroom. He forgot his reason for going in there and held out his arms to her. "You get out of that tub this instant, " he said. "And come dance the lindy with me."

And that's how I got my Uncle Harry.

Let's All Be Brothers

Everyone is as God has made him.
- Cervantes

When I taught kindergarten in the sixties, I was responsible for the February bulletin boards in the school. I wanted my pupils to make the decorations themselves because they would be so thrilled to see their own artwork in the front hall of the building. In January, I discussed the project with them. "February is Brotherhood Month," I said. "Do you know what brotherhood means?"

Pollyanna raised her hand. "It means friendship," she said.

"Very good!" I exclaimed. "Since February 14th is Valentine's Day, I thought we could make a bulletin board called LETS ALL BE VALENTINES. We could draw children from the four types of mankind holding hands and surround them with valentines that we made ourselves. We'll do one figure for each race. Won't that be fun?"

My children represented a variety of ethnic types. Jeffrey was Chinese and Ellen was Scandinavian. Mary Ann was Irish and Gregory was Black. Pollyanna was an amalgamation of Black, Indian, Caucasian and Jewish with a few Catholics and Baptists on her family tree. She was my brightest, most verbal child.

Everyone was very excited about designing valentines, but they didn't seem to understand what I meant about race. "We all have different color skins," I explained. "It identifies us. For example, Blacks have dark skin and Indians are red. Who knows someone who is Black?

I smiled a knowing smile at Gregory. Bobby Gray raised his hand. "Aunt Jemimah," he said.

I cleared my throat. "Yes, but what about someone you KNOW?"

Silence. I decided to switch tactics. "Does anyone know what a red man is called?" I asked.

Everyone knew that one. "An Indian!" shouted Gloria.

"Right," I said. "Now who would like to draw one of the four large figures for our board?"

After much involved discussion, Gregory volunteered to draw a white girl. "I want to do the red one," said Jeffrey. "My mama says I am really good at drawing Indians."

Bobby decided to paint a yellow man and Pollyanna volunteered to make a black woman. I gave each child a piece of paper as big as they were and a large box of crayons. "This is a big bulletin board," I said. "So make the figures as tall as you are. And remember to have their arms outstretched so all four races can hold hands."

They nodded to me as if they knew what I was talking about and began to draw. At the end of the hour, all four figures were finished. Gregory's white girl was as pale as a bleached sheet. Her eyes were an oatmeal color, her hair like raw meringue and she wore a purple skirt. "She's a dancer," he explained.

Jeffrey's red man was the color of a fire engine with a feather in its head. "Can I do the cowboy next?" he asked. "I am really SUPER at cowboys!"

Bobby's yellow man was bright as a rain slicker with green eyes and a black pigtail. It looked like a new design for a traffic signal. Pollyanna, who carried all the races within her, produced a black shape with white eyes that was suitable for Halloween.

I thought the pictures were very creative but if they were to be put on the hall bulletin board, they had to be a bit more explicit. Obviously, my class did not realize that these race divisions represented themselves. "Oriental people come from China, Japan and Korea and lots of other places in the South Pacific," I said. "They have yellow skin. We have some people from those places right here in this class! Can you name someone here from China?" and I smiled at Jeffrey.

Blank faces.

I tried again. "Where is your grandma from, Jeffrey?"

He looked mystified. "Vermont," he said.

I cleared my throat. "I am absolutely certain that you see yellow people every day, Jeffrey," I said. "And do you know where?"

The entire class was silent, their eyes filled with envy. Jeffrey looked at me with a mystified expression. "Where are they?" he asked.

I smiled. "At your dinner table!" I announced. "Who eats dinner with you, honey?"

Jeffrey thought for a moment and then he smiled. "Mommy, Daddy and Brenda," he said.

"Right," I said.

I looked at their expectant faces and tried again. "We have lots of black people in our room, too," I said. "Pollyanna, do any of them look like the person you drew for us?"

Pollyanna giggled. "Oh, Miss Miller!" she said. "No one anywhere is really black!" she said.

"What about Gregory?" I asked.

Now everyone was laughing. "Gregory?" said Pollyanna. "Why he's . . he's Gregory."

I paused for a moment and then I smiled. "Right!" I said. "Now I want everyone to hold up their portraits so we all can see how wonderful they are!"

Adults often forget that a person's skin doesn't identify anything that is significant about him. Understanding is the only direct route to the heart. Each one of us brings his own unique gift to humanity; a gift we could so easily recognize if we would see one another with the fresh eye of a five-year-old child.

After all, there is but one race: Humanity
George Moore